just put Nick out of her life.

Books you will enjoy
by CHARLOTTE LAMB

FRUSTRATION

Considering the tumultuous circumstances of their first meeting, it was hardly surprising that Jake Lang should despise and dislike Natalie Buchan. But their work threw them together and it was difficult for her to avoid him, with the inevitable result that she found herself falling in love with him. Would she ever be able to convince him that she saw him as something more than a substitute for her late husband?

LOVE IS A FRENZY

As a nightclub singer, Rachel was used to men's admiration—but seventeen-year-old Nicky Hammond was something different. His boyish devotion was sweet and touching—but Rachel couldn't possibly take it seriously, let alone return it; yet how could she convince his disapproving father Mark that she wasn't cradle-snatching—or worse?

DARK DOMINION

The marriage of Caroline and James Fox had run into serious trouble after only a short time—and the situation was not helped by the obvious fact that James was involved with another woman. But would anything be improved if Caroline turned to her old friend Jake, who made it clear that he wanted to be more than a friend . . .?

POSSESSION

Laura didn't like and didn't trust Dan Harland, and she couldn't understand why her grandfather thought so highly of him. It was obvious that Dan wanted to take control of the family firm—and that her grandfather was actually encouraging him to marry her as a means of doing so. And she was horribly afraid that Dan didn't just want possession of the firm; he wanted her too . . .

FEVER

BY

CHARLOTTE LAMB

MILLS & BOON LIMITED
17–19 FOLEY STREET
LONDON W1A 1DR

First published 1979
Australian copyright 1980
Philippine copyright 1980
This edition 1980

© Charlotte Lamb 1979

ISBN 0 263 73168 5

Set in Linotype Baskerville 11 on 12 pt.

Made and printed in Great Britain by
Richard Clay (The Chaucer Press), Ltd., Bungay, Suffolk

CHAPTER ONE

SARA was worried about Greg. She had barely taken her eyes off him since they arrived at the party although he was on the far side of the room, with a large circle of people around him, who were roaring with laughter at everything he said. People always laughed when Greg chose to make them. Although he looked like a sad clown he could be bitterly funny, his tongue like a rapier, annihilating with a phrase or pinning down character like a moth on a card.

Her host suddenly appeared beside her, bending to say: 'Miss Nichols, may I introduce . . .'

She wasn't listening although she gave a fixed, courteous smile in the vague direction of the man who was being introduced to her, offering her hand. It was taken, held, while their host, after a murmured apology, moved away. Sara kept her smile, but her eyes were still on Greg, trying to keep track of the number of drinks he had had.

Suddenly she realised that her hand had not been given back. She looked up then, her eyes focusing, and found herself being watched by hostile blue eyes.

'Can I have my hand back? I've always found two rather useful,' she said tartly, pulling free of his grip. Almost at once her eyes turned back towards

5

Greg, a concerned frown drawing her brows together.

She was aware of a voice speaking beside her and without realising it was giving automatic little smiles, nodding, as though listening, but actually merely wishing the stranger would go away. It was a shock when a hand suddenly clamped down on her wrist, swinging her round so that her gaze flew upwards in startled enquiry.

'You haven't heard a word I said, have you?'

She looked at him properly then, her catlike green eyes wide and sharp, absorbing the tall, powerful body and black hair, the harsh, strong lines of his face, realising that he had a face she would like to paint; drivingly individual with features which were at war with each other, a sensuality in the mould of his mouth which did not match the hard, cold blue eyes. Sara gave him a cool little smile.

'I'm sorry, Mr ...?' She broke off, unable to remember his name, and his face darkened.

'Rawdon,' he said with a bite. 'Nick Rawdon. We were just introduced, not that you noticed.'

'What do you do, Mr Rawdon?' she asked, because she had always found people loved to talk about themselves and if this stranger launched into a monologue it would give her a chance to watch Greg uninterrupted.

His eyes narrowed, their colour a blinding blue, holding her gaze. 'You don't give a damn what I do,' he retorted.

She didn't, but he was breaking the rules of polite conversation to state it openly, which surprised her, keeping her eyes on his face in curious enquiry.

'Is it a secret?' she asked, suddenly amused.

The curl of her mouth drew his attention. The blue eyes dropped to stare and she felt an abrupt heat coming into her face at something in the way he looked at her, then he glanced from her mouth to her eyes, one dark brow rising sardonically.

'Are you a spy?' Sara murmured, deliberately teasing now. 'Or do you do something one doesn't mention in polite society?'

'You've never heard of Rawdon's Bank?' he asked in a voice which was dry and incredulous.

'Oh, you're a bank,' she said mockingly, laughter in the green eyes now. 'Heavens, I've never met one before. I must put it in my diary. Today, I met a real live bank.'

'Very funny,' he said, but he wasn't laughing. 'Quite a wit, aren't you?'

She knew she was being childish, but at this moment she didn't care because he was trying to keep her attention from Greg and he was annoying her. Her lashes fluttered down to hide the quick flick of her eyes to the far side of the room. Greg was laughing and, thank God, he had empty hands. It was rare for him to drink, but when he did, he always went too far. He only drank when he was reckless, and tonight he was certainly in that mood.

'You're an artist, I gather? What do you paint?'

She turned again at the insistent questioning, sighing slightly, her irritation barely disguised.

'Landscapes,' she said curtly.

He placed one hand against the wall, lounging in

front of her, blocking her view of Greg, and she suddenly had the suspicion that he did it deliberately, that he knew she was trying to keep track of what was happening over there. Her eyes lifted again to his face and found him staring down at her, the black bar of his brows meeting over his eyes. Sara tilted her head, her red-gold hair glittering in the light as she moved, and his blue eyes took on an open insolence, slowly wandering down her body in a fashion little short of insult.

She had been unaware of herself all evening, but now under those insolent eyes she was forced to become briefly conscious of the daring nature of her low-cut dress, the silver drift of it outlining every curve of her body. Greg had chosen it, teasing her. She had nothing in her wardrobe which would have done for this party, but it infuriated her to blush like a schoolgirl and she wished Greg had not persuaded her to wear it.

At that moment she caught the movement of Greg's hand as he lifted a glass to his mouth and was horrified to see him tip the whole contents down his throat. My God, at this rate he'll be roaring drunk soon, she thought. Drunk, Greg became outrageously frank and his frankness could have lasting consequences if he offended the people here tonight, people he hoped would offer him commissions.

She walked away towards him without a word, leaving Nick Rawdon staring after her with a savage expression.

She slid a hand through Greg's arm and he looked

down at her, kissing her on her small nose.

'Home, buster,' she said softly.

Greg grinned again recklessly. He was a tall, thin man of thirty-four, his hair thick and curly, the colour of melting toffee, a warm golden brown. His brown eyes could be remote, they could be mocking. His features were sensitive and intelligent but filled with melancholy, attractive in an ugly-handsome way. Women found his sad, funny face highly attractive. The glamour of his sudden smile made conquests in the most unlikely places.

'Keeping an eye on me, darling?' he asked her lightly now. 'Not counting my drinks, I hope.'

He knew she was and their exchanged smiles admitted it.

'Come on, Greg,' she said easily.

From the circle behind him she caught Lorna Robert's eye and gave her a polite smile which was not returned. Lorna detested her. For the past three years she had been crazy about Greg, who fled her like a hunted fawn, his brown eyes rueful. Lorna persisted in believing that Greg's evasions were due to Sara. She would not accept that Greg just did not fancy her.

Greg slide an arm round her waist and they moved away together, Sara's slender body seductive in the silvery gauze dress which gave tantalising glimpses of her as she walked.

'Had a good party?'

Sara shrugged. 'You did, I noticed.'

'You noticed everything, little sharp eyes.'

'I'm driving home,' she said as they moved towards their host, and Greg gave her a laughing, mock irate glance.

'You aren't suggesting I'm intoxicated!'

'Not while you can still say it, but any minute now,' she retorted.

'The Leith police dismisseth us,' he intoned piously. '*And* I can walk a chalk line.'

'Show-off!'

Their host was a stockbroker who also happened to own a number of racehorses, one of which Greg had recently painted after it won a final brilliant race before retiring to a stud farm. The heavily built man shook hands with Greg warmly, his bald head glistening under the lights.

'Good of you to come.' He launched into a second string of compliments about the painting and Greg smiled sweetly at him as he listened. Sara was relieved to be getting him away before he reached the stage where he told the man precisely what he thought of him. Greg was well aware that his commission owed more to the fact that his work was already appreciating and therefore was a good investment, than to any real admiration the man had for his work.

A movement behind her made their host glance over her shoulder and a totally different smile broke over his cherubic pink face, a look of real awe and respect.

'Nick, my dear fellow!' he breathed, beaming wider. 'I was just telling Mr Halliday here how pleased we are with his painting. You must run down to my place some time and see it.'

Sara half turned, her eyes lifting, and found the hard blue eyes on her profile. Nick Rawdon shifted slightly to face Greg, holding out his hand.

Their host obliged quickly. 'Mr Halliday, this is Nick Rawdon.'

Greg shook hands, the rapid thrust of his gaze moving over the other man, interest in his brown eyes.

'He's a bank,' Sara told him. 'Fascinating, isn't it?'

Their host looked blankly at her, but Greg's eyes lit up.

'A bank? Really?' He gazed limpidly at Nick Rawdon. 'Do you give cheques or only receive them?'

'Banks never give anything.' Sara reminded him. 'They take it and they keep it. Great big iron bars on their strongrooms and computers clicking away night and day. What an exciting life!'

Nick Rawdon didn't say a word, he just watched Sara with that cold, blue stare, the taut bones of his face immobile. She did not look at him; she was grinning at Greg. But she was aware of his eyes and vaguely of the emotions behind them. It didn't bother her since she was unlikely ever to see Nick Rawdon again, and this was amusing Greg, it was lifting him out of the black depression which had been engulfing him all day. For that, Sara would sacrifice almost anything.

A tray passed within reach and Greg's hand moved to take a glass. Sara caught it, drew it down beside her, holding it tightly, and Greg slid an ironic glance at her, his mouth quizzical.

She shook her head very slightly at him, her green eyes steadily loving, and Greg shrugged.

'We must go,' he said abruptly, and without a word or a look to the others he pulled her after him towards the door.

Sara drove them home. Greg lolled beside her in the passenger seat, his hands in his pockets, staring into the lamplit darkness. Now that he had left the party, his face had lapsed into brooding melancholy.

Sara had already forgotten the tall, dark figure of Nick Rawdon. She was consumed with anxiety as the car turned into the garage of their home. Greg wandered off into the house while she was closing the garage door and when she went inside she found him on the phone. She went into the kitchen and began to make coffee.

Greg came whistling in a moment later and she looked round, her eyes eager.

'He's better, the injections are taking hold.'

'Thank God!' She wound her arms round Greg's waist and put her head on his shoulder. 'You really shouldn't have gone to that party, Greg. You should have stayed at home tonight.'

'I'd have gone crazy,' Greg said. He opened the fridge and took out a prepared stick of celery, bit into it with a crunch of white teeth.

She turned to get down cups. 'How was she?' Her voice was very casual.

'Fine,' Greg said as casually. 'I think I'll have a shower. I'll have that coffee later.'

When he had gone Sara finished making the

coffee and left it for a moment, staring out of the window at the dark garden. The calm lines of Greg's face as he left the room had not deceived her. Lucy would have been exhausted, drained, and that would hurt Greg, hurt him the more because he could not, dare not, show how much he cared.

Sometimes Sara wished to God that Greg had never met Rob and Lucy. No, she corrected herself at once, grimacing, that wasn't true. Both Greg and herself loved Lucy and Rob. Everyone loved Rob. He was a darling lamb, the kindest man you could wish to meet. Severely crippled by a progressive illness, he spent his life between his bed and a wheelchair, yet he made everyone laugh whenever they saw him, he was witty in a warm, sweet way which held no unkindness. Greg's humour had a black tinge to it at times, but she had never heard Rob say a word against anyone. His wife, Lucy, adored him. He was her life. She looked at him with love whenever her eyes touched him.

It was a tragic irony that Greg, who was so self-sufficient, so clever, so strong, should fall deeply and hopelessly in love with Lucy. He had never, in Sara's presence, given a hint, a sign, of his feelings to Lucy herself. Sara only knew about it because, drunk and therefore reckless, he had blurted it out to her, later wishing to God he had never said a word. Sara had sworn never to mention it to a living soul; Greg had made her swear to that. Particularly he did not want Lucy or Rob to know.

There had always been a strong, close relationship between Sara and Greg. They shared a house largely because of force of circumstances. They were not linked by any blood tie, but their parents, both having lost a partner in middle life, had married each other and lived very happily together until their deaths. Greg and Sara had both lived with them and so the house, eventually, became their joint property. They might have sold it and shared the proceeds, but they decided to go on living together because it was easier.

For the sake of privacy rather than any idea of propriety, they had had the house divided into two flats. Sara had the downstairs flat, Greg the upstairs, largely because it was Sara who did all the laundering and so needed access to the garden more often. She did all the gardening, too. Greg's idea of a garden was to have a lawn on which he could paint or sunbathe. Sara loved pottering around the garden. She had a functioning garden—vegetables, fruit bushes, herbs. She liked to cook with vegetables she had freshly picked that morning. It gave food a better flavour.

If they had moved in different circles, eyebrows might have been raised at the way they lived, but they were both artists and their friends merely accepted their relationship on the face of it. Sara thought of Greg as her brother and she knew Greg cared for her in the same way. What the world thought did not bother her. They had lived together for twelve years altogether now, ever since his father married her mother. It was due to Greg that Sara had gone to art school. She owed him a debt she could never repay. She knew him better than anyone in the world did and she loved him.

Watching Greg with Lucy she sometimes wondered if she had imagined his confession. Greg was a past master at pretence. He smiled at Lucy casually, he joked with her and Rob, he was at ease with them, friendly, cheerful, never betraying any emotion.

Only once or twice Sara had caught the merest flicker in him. One Christmas two years ago Lucy had kissed him under the mistletoe at a party, her eyes teasing. Greg had grinned back, but he had been white as he turned away, a look in his eyes making Sara feel sick.

She had never been in love herself. Now and then she had played with the idea, amusing herself by pretending to be in love, but somehow the real thing had never hit her. Watching Greg, she was often glad about that. His love for Lucy dominated his life, although it never showed on the surface. Sara knew that in a cupboard in his flat were sheaves of sketches of Lucy. They never saw the light of day. Greg had only shown them to her once, the night he told her about the way he felt. They had been incredibly good, so acute and yet passionate that she had been moved and horrified. She had a fear that Greg would destroy them one day and that would be tragic because they were the best thing he had ever done, but he was afraid that one day Lucy might see them and then she would know about him. That was something Greg could not bear. He would fight like mad to stop Lucy guessing.

It had increased Sara's respect for Greg to watch

him with Rob, to see the genuine love and caring he gave Lucy's husband. Greg often sat with Rob to give Lucy a break. He would draw cartoons for Rob, making the other choke with laughter at the wicked, perceptive humour. He would read aloud to him. It even tired Rob to hold a book these days; his hands were weakened by the disease. Greg casually attended to Rob's physical needs like a brother, lifting him in and out of his chair, the wiry thin strength of his body astonishing. Rob was much heavier than Greg. It was difficult for Lucy to do these things—she was a slight, small woman. Greg welcomed the chance to ease the problems her life piled on to her shoulders.

For the last few days Rob had been appreciably worse, in much more pain, and Greg had been tense with anxiety over it. Now Sara heard him whistling as he showered and knew that he was limp with relief because Rob had responded to the new treatment. It was only a temporary relief; there was no long-term cure. But at least Rob was better for the moment.

She went up to yell to him to hurry before the coffee was ruined. 'I've left a cup in your sitting-room,' she told him through the door. 'Goodnight.'

He called back cheerfully, 'Goodnight, darling.' Sara went down to her own part of the house and got ready for bed, slipping into it with a sigh. It had been a wearing evening and she was glad it was over. Lying in the darkness she had a brief memory of a cold, dark face and blindingly bright blue eyes. What had his name been? She couldn't remember for a second, then it came back. Nick. Nick the bank, she thought, giggling. He had looked furious when she and Greg were playing the fool, but at least it had briefly lifted Greg's sadness.

She dismissed him and settled to sleep.

Greg went off early next morning to call in and see Rob before he took off for Cambridgeshire to see a horse. His paintings of horses had made his name. They were commanding high prices these days, but Greg painted them because he had a passion for horses, he loved their nobility and grace, the sheen of their coats, their elegant visual lines.

He wouldn't be back for several days, and when he did get back it would be Sara's turn to dash off, because she had a commission to paint a sombre Yorkshire hillside for the owner of a hotel who wanted a view of it to hang in his foyer.

When Greg had gone, Sara took her sketchpad out into the garden intending to do some life drawings of birds. She wore her customary working gear; well-washed old blue jeans and a white T-shirt which had shrunk and now fitted her rather too closely. She worked for an hour and then found the sunshine too tempting to resist. Sprawling on the lawn, she closed her eyes, her arms curved above her head, letting the warmth soak into her.

A step startled her and she opened her eyes hurriedly and stared in disbelief at the dark face of Nick Rawdon. Sara felt herself flush, ludicrously at a disadvantage lying there at his feet, the long hard body looming over her. He was aware of it, too. His mouth had a satisfied twist as he watched her.

'Remember me?' he asked mockingly, one dark brow curving upwards.

'Yes,' she said shortly, sitting up, conscious of dishevelled clothes and grass in her hair.

'You surprise me,' he drawled. 'I got the impression you never even saw me.'

'What do you want?' she asked uneasily, wishing he would stop staring at her so that she could get to her feet without feeling ungainly.

'I got your address from our host last night,' he told her, as though she had asked him quite another question. Reluctantly she got to her feet, still finding herself looking up at him, since he was well over six foot and she was only five foot four.

'You look very different this afternoon,' he murmured, eyeing her with a glance that followed faithfully every warm curve of her body in the over-tight shirt and jeans, and then came back to observe with amusement the warmth which had filled her skin. He took a step nearer, the blue eyes taunting. 'Not feeling quite so funny?'

He hadn't liked it when she laughed at him, when she and Greg made fun of his bank, she realised, which wasn't surprising. She had been behaving badly, but she had been anxious over Greg. She hadn't cared what Nick Rawdon thought.

Something of this showed in her angry green eyes. He watched her, the hard lines of his face tightening.

'If it's about a commission, Mr Rawdon,' she said quietly, 'Greg is away at the moment. He won't be back for a few days. Can I get him to ring you?'

His face had altered, a dark red coming into his cheeks, his blue eyes taking on an icy glare. 'He lives here? With you?' The harsh note in his voice made her move back slightly, alarmed.

'Well, yes, of course. Didn't you know?'

His sensual lips had become a straight, fierce line. He parted them to ask curtly, 'You're not married, are you?' It was more statement than question and it had the ring of contempt.

She saw then what he was thinking and because she was so used to living openly in the same house with Greg without anyone lifting an eyebrow, she began to laugh. 'No, of course not.' About to go on to explain her relationship with Greg, she was cut short by a clipped retort from him.

'Stupid of me to ask, wasn't it? I should have remembered you were both artists. Marriage is an outdated shibboleth, I suppose? You don't need it.'

'Don't put words in my mouth, buster,' she threw back, infuriated, the vivid red of her hair tossed back from her small face. 'I can do my own talking.'

'Your manners are appalling, Miss Nichols,' he said furiously, taking hold of her elbows and shaking her like a doll between his lean hands. 'As bad as your morals, apparently, but I don't expect you to share my view.'

'I wouldn't want to share anything with you,' Sara retorted, green eyes glittering.

'Wouldn't you?' he said in sudden barbed mockery, and before she could evade him he had bent his black head and taken her mouth violently, surprising her lips into parting for him, hungrily probing and demanding in a kiss which was more insult than pleasure. She was too astonished to struggle or respond, and before she had had time to realise what was happening, he pushed her away and turned on his heel, walking back the way he had come, round the side of the house.

She stared after him, a hand to her mouth, her lips stinging, filled with bruised heat.

She was too astonished to move for several minutes. She had been kissed before, but never on such short acquaintance or with such deliberate violence. The experience lingered in her mind all day. The slightly swollen look of her lips kept reminding her. She would put a finger to them, frowning. Why had he come? Had he wanted to see Greg about a commission? Or had he come to see her?

That thought was oddly disturbing. She was not unaware of her own looks, but her passion for work had made her almost indifferent to them. She had other things on her mind most of the time. Although she had a number of men friends, she had never had a lover. She had never let herself drift into a love affair because it might interfere with her work. Her few flirtations had been brief, a mere game, but once or twice she had been told by a would-be lover that she was beautiful. Sara had never taken these compliments seriously since her trained eye ruefully warned her of imperfections in herself which made beauty impossible.

She had fine-boned sensitive features; a delicate little nose, slanting green eyes with gold-tipped lashes, high cheekbones and smooth creamy skin, but Sara was too well aware that her mouth was far too wide for her face, far too generously cut, the fullness of the lower lip promising a passion which her cool green eyes denied.

Slender and slight in most respects, her body had a lack of proportion too; her breasts fuller and more rounded than her thin hips, so that she preferred to wear jeans and a shirt since she could not find many dresses which she could wear. From the back she could look like a boy, but when she turned the thrust of her breasts gave her a sexy outline which made men stare in interest.

She had been so intent on Greg at the party that Nick Rawdon had only just impinged on her consciousness, but he had forced himself into her mind now. She could not get that hard kiss out of her head, questions buzzing inside her whenever she thought of him.

When Greg returned she told him about the little incident and he raised his brows, comic irony in his face.

'Fancied you, you think?'

'I hadn't noticed,' Sara said. 'Men usually make that rather more obvious. I remember thinking he was downright hostile.'

'You did seem to be teasing him rather at that party,' Greg pointed out. 'I saw him watching you as if he'd like to hit you.'

'Maybe that's why he kissed me, then,' she murmured, grinning. 'It was a substitute for a slap round the face.'

'You sound almost regretful,' Greg teased. 'Would you have liked the slap better.'

'The way he kisses there wasn't much difference,' she shrugged.

'That's a mind-blowing thought,' Greg drawled, his brows quivering with amusement. 'I wish I'd been here.'

'Just as well you weren't. He'd got the impression we were living in sin.'

'What?' Greg stared.

'He seems to think that sharing a house can only mean one thing. A very narrow-minded man, Mr Rawdon.'

'Hence the kiss?' Greg looked angry suddenly. 'He thought you were an easy target, did he? I'd like to punch his handsome nose for him!'

That thought hadn't occurred to her until then and she flushed hotly, her eyes becoming very green.

'He's quite a high flyer, you know,' Greg went on thoughtfully. 'I read something about him and his bank the other day. An old merchant bank, it seems, with pretty hefty assets.' He grinned at her. 'No wonder he expected you to recognise his name!'

'And genuflect,' she said scornfully. 'He was mad because I didn't go all weak at the knees at the thought of all his money.'

'Well, next time you bump into him, darling, curtsey respectfully,' Greg drawled lightly.

'There won't be a next time,' Sara shrugged. 'I don't move in the sort of circles frequented by rich merchant bankers and I've a feeling he won't be coming back.'

'He might want me to paint a horse,' Greg pointed out. 'He's rich enough to own a stableful, but he somehow doesn't look like a racing man to me.'

'He looks as though he only has one hobby—counting his money.' Sara yawned. 'Oh, let's forget him—he's a boring subject, anyway. Now, I'm off to Yorkshire tomorrow, remember. I've left the fridge well stocked, but do try to eat fresh food now and then, Greg.'

'Yes, ma'am,' he said piously, pulling at his fore-lock.

'Liar,' she groaned. 'You won't even bother. You're worse than a child!'

'But you love me,' he said, blowing her a kiss.

'You're the only brother I've got,' she grimaced. 'Even if you are semi-detached.'

'You mean semi-attached,' he corrected.

'I know what I mean,' Sara said drily, and Greg gave her an amused, comprehending smile.

Next day she drove out of London en route for the north, rueful as she became entangled in the heavy motorway traffic streaming away from the capital, her head already totally clear of all recollection of Nick Rawdon, her mind moving ahead to the picture she was going to paint. Sara had an enormous capacity for self-protection, defending herself against troubling intrusion by blocking out anything that bothered her, so that she could get on with the job in hand. Since the death of their shared parents, Greg was the only human being who really mattered to her. She had a warm nature, but she had learnt to curb it, giving out freely only to Greg, and even then doing so under Greg's own rules, always keeping it light, laughing, never imposing demands on him or allowing any emotion to show. Greg's nature had formed her own, or rather rough-hewn it, shaping it to match his. Under the gay flippancy of their banter a real affection ran, but Sara was unaware of any other potential in herself, the passion her mouth hinted at always held back under the control of her cool green eyes.

CHAPTER TWO

THREE days later she was in York, doing some shopping, her feet aching after several hours spent walking around the narrow, crowded streets of the city. It was not her first visit to York, but each time she came she found new beauty to admire, new places to be fascinated by, her eye continually drawn to the irregular lines of the old houses and shops which tumbled down the hills on which the city had been built. It was necessarily a place in which one walked. Traffic was appalling and confusing. The most sensible thing to do was park the car in one of the car-parks outside the central core of the city and walk in to the main streets. Sara had come to buy paints, but she had been continually distracted by what she saw and her visit had been more protracted than she had intended.

She was staying in the hotel whose owner had

commissioned her. He was a short, sturdy man with a quick deep voice, his thinning hair turning grey. The hillside he wished her to paint was his obsession, she had discovered. A view of it greeted him each morning as he drew the curtains in his bedroom, he informed her, and he loved it more as time passed. Sara liked people who felt like that about places. A sense of place was bitten into her own mind. That was why she painted landscapes, trying to give stark illumination to the essentials of each place she painted. She had spent her first day merely talking to her client, getting from him the feel and atmosphere he wanted her to convey and deciding how far she agreed with him. Luckily, they agreed very well.

His hotel was an old public house in a road which led off the main route from York to Scarborough. The rugged white lines of the building looked charming against the deep green curves of the hills. It had at first occurred to Sarah to paint the hotel against the rolling setting it enjoyed, but her client wanted one particular view and no other. He wanted a permanent reminder of his beloved hillside.

'I'd rather have painted it in the winter,' Sara had sighed, smiling at him. 'It must be very beautiful then.'

'It's lovely now,' he had said obstinately. 'I want the oaks and that elm there and all the wall. Some sheep too.'

He was a man who knew what he wanted. Sara had grinned at him, accepting his insistence.

First she had done some sketches which she had

discussed with him at length and now she was about to start on the actual picture, but she had had an accident with her paints. Struggling with them the day before she had dropped several and a car had rolled over them before she could pick them up. The little incident had annoyed her, meaning a delay, but now she was glad she had come to York again. The morning had been delightful.

Glancing at her watch she realised that it was lunchtime and she was hungry. There were a number of places where she could eat, but she remembered a small bistro down near the river, so she turned back that way, smiling as she passed a long crocodile of schoolchildren on their way back from the Castle Museum. They were chattering, groaning, eating ice lollies in a surreptitious way, the teachers leading them looking round suspiciously now and then.

Still smiling with amusement, Sara hurried on and ran full tilt into a man coming out of a modern office block. She looked up casually to apologise, her hands on the chest into which she had walked, and her smile died as she recognised the cold blue eyes of Nick Rawdon.

It was so unexpected that she couldn't think of a thing to say, her face reflected her dismay.

To her own irritation she found herself blushing hotly and, to cover her embarrassment, said flippantly: 'Fancy running into you!'

He was not amused. He put his own hands over hers and drew them down from his body, dropping her hands before pushing his own into his trouser pockets, the thrust of his arms pushing open his jacket to show a sexily close-tailored waistcoat which emphasised his slim waist, and a formal blue-and-white striped shirt. He looked different, she thought, trying to decide what gave her that impression. After a moment she realised that it was his clothes. They were far more stiffly elegant than the suits he had worn on their previous two meetings. He looked what he was in them; a man accustomed to authority, assured, tough, impressive.

'What are *you* doing in York?' he asked with a hint of accusation, as though he suspected her of following him here.

Her colour and breathing had returned to normal. She threw back her head in an unthinking gesture of defiance and his eyes followed the movement to catch the glint of sunlight on the rioting red-gold hair.

'What are *you*?' she retorted.

His hard mouth twisted at her avoidance of his question. 'Working. I'm here for a conference.'

She glanced up at the block he had left. 'Bankers Anonymous?'

The flash of his eyes told her he didn't like that. But he kept his cool, his lips ironic. 'Haven't you got a bank account, Miss Nichols? Or does Halliday see to all that for you?'

It was her turn to be furious, but she followed his example and hid her anger, smiling with cold sweetness at him, her eyes very vivid and brilliant.

'Oh, I keep my money in a sock.'

'If I believed you I would think you a fool.' He

dismissed her claim with a shrug of those broad
shoulders which made her notice the beautiful fit
of his jacket, the smooth tailoring and cut of it.
None of her male friends wore clothes like these.
She imagined they must cost a fortune. 'And what
are *you* doing in York?'

'Painting,' she retorted. 'Like you, I'm working.'

'In York itself?'

'No,' Sara said, shaking her head. 'I'm painting a
landscape in a village a few miles away. I came into
York to do some shopping.'

He glanced at her then away, his heavy lids half
lowered, a cynical glint in the blue eyes. 'Halliday
with you?'

'No,' Sara retorted, her rounded chin lifted in
challenge. 'Greg's at home.' A faint indulgence came
into her eyes unwittingly. 'Starving himself to death,
probably. If I'm not there, he forgets to eat.'

'How sad,' he muttered, his lips twisting.

She stiffened at the tone and said shortly, 'Which
reminds me, I've got to find somewhere to eat, myself. Goodbye, Mr Rawdon.'

As she turned to walk round him he caught her
arm, his long fingers tight around her skin. 'Have
lunch with me. I was just on my way to eat.'

She looked down at his hand. 'No, thank you.'
Catching his eye, she felt impelled to make some
excuse, adding, with a glance down at her old jeans
and then his expensive clothes, 'We don't match. I
can't see you eating in a cheap bistro.'

'We'll lunch at my hotel,' he returned calmly.

She shook her head. 'Not in these jeans.'

'We can eat in my suite. No one will notice your clothes.'

That amused her, the idea of him having a suite all to himself. He caught the smile she involuntarily gave and his blue eyes betrayed anger again. He thought she was laughing at him once more.

'I'm sorry,' she said, sobering. 'It's just that we're from such different worlds. I've no doubt your hotel does a fantastic lunch, Mr Rawdon, but I'll stick to my bistro, if you don't mind.'

'I do mind,' he said, staring at her. 'Are you an inverted snob, Miss Nichols?'

'No, just a realist. We come from different sides of the track and I prefer my side.'

'Then why were you at that party the other night?'

'Greg was there to drum up business,' she said drily. 'I was there because he wanted me there.'

'You're his window dressing, are you? He uses you as bait for customers?'

The insult took her breath away. 'Watch yourself, mister,' she said between her teeth. 'You may be bigger than me, but that won't stop me batting you over the head with a blunt instrument!'

He laughed, looking astonished, and just then another party of schoolchildren rushed past them and knocked into Sara, throwing her forward so that she was flung against Nick Rawdon, forced into his body, her hands instinctively grasping his shoulders to retain her balance. His arm went round her to steady her, and she looked up involuntarily. They were so close that she could see the faint flecks of black in his blue eyes which gave that depth of colour from a distance. Suddenly she realised his eyes were nearer and then he was lowering his head with his gaze fixed on her mouth. She couldn't believe it, yet she realised he was going to kiss her. Even as she became aware of his intention he jerked back his head with an almost visible effort, his face taut. Their eyes met and he looked away at once.

'My hotel's just round the corner over the bridge,' he said in brusque tones.

Sara had not meant to lunch with him, but she found herself walking meekly with him through the busy streets, because she was still suffering from the shock of realising that he had almost kissed her. He just didn't look like the sort of man who kissed in public places. As he led her into the smoothly carpeted foyer of his modern hotel she eyed him curiously, wondering suddenly if it was wise to go up to his suite with him. Did that hard kiss in her garden count as a pass? He hardly looked the type to try for a rapid conquest over lunch, but you could never tell. She didn't fancy trying to fight him off over smoked salmon and steak. He was a tough-looking customer under that smooth suit. Alone in his suite she might find she had bitten off more than she could chew, particularly as he seemed convinced she was on the promiscuous side.

All the way up to his top floor suite she was debating how to deal with whatever situation she might face. He ushered her into the spacious sitting-room and picked up the telephone beside the enormous television.

'What would you like? I was going to have a steak.'

'How surprising,' she said drily.

He gave her an unsmiling look, noting the sarcasm. 'In hotels I find it's one item on the menu which I can be sure is freshly cooked.'

She shrugged. 'Steak will be fine.'

'How gracious,' he said, and she flushed.

'I'm sorry, I wasn't intending to be ill-mannered.'

'That's all right, Miss Nichols. I'm getting accustomed to your sharp little tongue.'

He picked up the little booklet and looked up the number for room service, dialling, his black head bent.

There were french windows open at one end of the long room. Sara wandered through them to find herself on a balcony over the river. She leaned on the iron balustrade and stared down. Green banks were feathered with flowering elder, white petals of it blown across the sleepy water. A man with a sun-flushed head slept in a deck chair on the grass, the sun drawing beads of perspiration from his bald head. Some ducks paddled silently past like Indians in a surprise war party, their little black eyes sliding to inspect him for signs of food.

She heard a footstep behind her but did not turn. Nick Rawdon stood at her shoulder and she heard him breathing. He didn't speak and after a few moments she turned her head to give him an interrogative glance. He was staring at her profile, she found, and as she looked at him their eyes met. A curious shiver ran down her spine.

'You're very beautiful,' he murmured huskily.

The remark bothered her, so she gave him a brief smile and turned away again, glancing along the old wharves bordering the far side of the river.

'What sort of relationship do you have with Halliday?' he asked quietly. 'Does he turn a blind eye if you have other men?'

She turned angrily. 'Look, you're under a misapprehension, Mr Rawdon. Greg is my stepbrother, not my lover.'

His eyes narrowed, blindingly blue, penetrating. 'You don't live alone with him, then? Your parents live there too?'

'They died some years ago,' she explained politely but coldly.

His dark brows lifted cynically. 'So you do live alone together?'

'Not in the sense you mean. In everything but the blood tie, we're brother and sister.'

He smiled sardonically. 'If you say so.'

He didn't believe her, the cynical blue eyes told her that, and Sara was furious for a moment. Then she shrugged. Did she care if he believed her or not? She didn't much like him. Oh, he was unquestionably sexy in a hard, aggressive fashion, but he didn't turn her on. Let him think what he chose! He probably preferred to believe that she led a wild, immoral life just because she painted.

Her small face held contempt as she smiled at him. 'You have a narrow, conventional mind, Mr Rawdon.'

'*Do* I?' His mouth tightened.

'That's your hang-up, not mine. Think what you like.'

'Thanks for the permission. I intended to do so anyway.'

'I'm sure you did. It would take a tin-opener to find a crack in that closed little mind of yours.'

'Thanks,' he said with a bite of his white teeth. 'You don't like me, do you?'

'Not much,' she said frankly, her eyes on his face. 'You're hardly my man of the year, but then I scarcely know you. Maybe you have hidden charms. To some women your money might make you acceptable.'

She heard him draw a harsh breath. 'One day I might just slap you senseless,' he said in a voice which meant every word.

She was so surprised by the threat that she laughed. 'Oh, I'm sure you wouldn't lay hands on a woman.'

'On you I would,' he said almost as though he enjoyed the prospect. 'With pleasure.'

She fluttered her lashes at him, grinning. 'I'm shocked. And I thought you were a gentleman. An upstanding banker shouldn't say such things.'

He stared into her vivid, laughing face and moved a step nearer with an expression on his face that startled her. At that moment the waiter arrived with their lunch and Nick Rawdon turned away abruptly. What had he been about to do? she wondered. Kiss her or hit her? She wasn't sure which, but there had been something in his face, that much she knew.

The thin little waiter laid their meal out on the table on the balcony, giving Sara a quick smooth look before he left. Although his face betrayed nothing, she could imagine what he was thinking. Men like Nick Rawdon did not bring women to their suite without a certain motive and the quarrel she had just had with him seemed to her something of a relief. He wasn't likely to try to inveigle her into bed after that exchange.

She sat down and watched Nick pour the wine. The wind from the river lifted her short hair and flung it into a glittering tangle. The ducks idled past on the river, so she leaned over and crumbled her roll into the air, laughing as they snapped in astonishment at the crumbs drifting down to them.

'Lucky ducks,' she said, dusting her hands. 'Manna from heaven.'

'Yes,' he murmured, his eyes on her. 'Eat your steak before it gets cold.'

While they ate they talked, a little stiffly at first, making polite conversation. Nick did not seem hungry, pushing away his meal half-eaten. 'Tell me about yourself,' he commanded.

She gave him a wry, mocking smile. 'Yes, sir.'

'Please,' he added with a twist of his lips that admitted that he had been dictatorial.

'What do you want to know?'

'Everything,' he said, and Sara stared at him, finding herself blushing again, for no reason.

She looked away and talked lightly about her parents, her childhood, Greg, her years at art school and her career since. Whenever she paused he asked her a question, showing that he had not only followed everything she said but was interested. She was barely conscious of the passage of time, enjoying the golden afternoon light, the distant ripple of the water, the moving shadows of the trees below. Suddenly he glanced at his watch, his face reluctant.

'I'm afraid I have to get back to the conference. Will you stay in York and have dinner with me?'

She felt a pang of alarm because she was tempted to do as he asked and she knew it was madness. Smiling politely she said, 'How kind, but I'm afraid I have to get back.'

'Must you?' His eyes were level, holding hers. 'I can offer you a very good dinner.'

'I'm sorry,' she said. It wasn't the dinner, it was afterwards that bothered her. She had the strong suspicion that he didn't intend the evening's entertainment to stop at food.

She smiled though, because he had given her a pleasant lunch. It had been very enjoyable eating on this balcony overlooking the river. If he hadn't been who he was, she might even have wanted to see him again, because she was finding him increasingly attractive, but it wouldn't do.

'I want to see you again,' he said in a voice which held a reluctance akin to her own, as though he too knew that it was absurd to pursue the acquaintance.

She looked at him frankly. 'That wouldn't be a good idea. We have nothing in common.'

She had stood up and he had risen too, but now he moved close to her and put his hand around her neck, his fingers threading their way into her hair, the tips of them slowly caressing her hidden nape.

'I could prove you wrong,' he said in a thick, slurred voice, and she felt her breath catch as she became aware of the meaning of that look in his eyes. He was staring at her mouth with his lids half-veiling the glitter of his blue gaze.

Her first instinct was to get angry. Her long training from Greg altered that impulse to a flippant mockery.

'I'm not a toy for bored bankers,' she grinned at him.

Greg liked her to talk like that. It hid thoughts and feelings Greg thought best hidden. Sara had grown up teasing, mocking, playing it cool, but she was beginning to know that this man found her flippancy maddening. He did not appreciate mockery and he was angry now. His eyes shot temper at her.

'Take me seriously, Sara,' he said in a warning tone.

'I don't want to take you any way at all,' she threw back in a voice as angry as his because he refused to play the game by her rules.

'I want to take you,' he came back at once, his voice thickening. 'In every way possible.'

Her face burned. She could not laugh back at words, a tone, like that. It left her breathless, off balance.

'Thanks for the warning, Mr Rawdon,' she said quickly, angrily. 'If I needed an excuse for not seeing you again, you just gave it to me. Get this, and get it for good, Mr Rawdon, I'm not available. Not now, not ever!' She gave him a last icy, pointed look and turned to walk out of the suite. He stood there without moving, watching her walk away.

She took the lift down to the foyer and almost

ran out of the hotel. She had never in her life been
so shaken. Men had sometimes propositioned her
in the past, but always obliquely, leaving her room
to refuse without causing offence, and she had never
once had to walk out on anybody because if she
didn't she might hit them over the head with a
chair.

Nick Rawdon had taken her breath away, not
merely by what he said, but by how he said it, his
tone stupefying her. He hadn't been being funny.
He had meant every word and the hard blue eyes
had been acquisitive as they looked at her body.

Driving out of York she got lost, which wasn't surprising in her shattered frame of mind, especially
as the one-way system and the road signs were, she
decided, deliberately misleading as though put there
by malignant spirits. It took her some time to find
her way out of the city, and as she drove she could
not get Nick Rawdon out of her mind.

She tried, angrily. Their meeting had been an
unlucky trick of fate and she had never hesitated
as she refused to see him again, but she had to
admit she found him attractive. She would have
liked to deny it, even to herself. She would have
liked him to be a dwarf of fifty with a bald head,
a paunch and nasty little eyes. That was how she had
always imagined merchant bankers. She saw them
like characters from an old fairy story about a
dwarf who hoarded money and jewels, and always
got his long grey beard trapped in logs and rocks.
A banker had no business to look like Nick Rawdon, with a face that seemed to have been chiselled

out of concrete and eyes that pierced and glittered like blue stones. She wished she could have been blind to the attractions of that lithe, powerful body, seeing nothing but his formal city suit and striped shirt.

Their worlds orbited in opposite directions. They had nothing in common, despite his attempt to make her believe they had.

'And I can guess why,' she muttered aloud, amusing another driver as he shot past her out of the traffic jam she had found herself trapped in outside York.

Mr Nick Rawdon had been hoping to give her bed as well as board that evening. He imagined that because she shared Greg's house, she was ready to share other things with other men. He could think again!

When she got back to the hotel she rang Greg to make sure he was eating. He sounded very far away, his voice remote, but then he was probably working and Greg did not like being interrupted when he was at work. His mind could be absorbed so entirely that he often did not even hear the telephone. She was lucky he had answered it this time.

She hesitated before mentioning that she had seen Nick Rawdon, but when she did tell him Greg sounded interested.

'What a coincidence! Did he make another pass?'

She hesitated again and Greg laughed softly.

'I gather he did. Persistent fellow, isn't he?'

'It wasn't funny,' she said almost feverishly, and her tone sobered Greg.

'Did he really bother you, sweetheart?' Greg knew how inexperienced Sara was under her modern, flip manner. He sounded concerned, a faint anxiety creeping into his voice.

'I was furious,' she said, unable to pretend amusement, because she could still hear the tone in which Nick Rawdon had spoken to her, and it was sending shivers down her spine just remembering.

'Do you want me to come up there?' Greg asked, which meant that he was now taking this seriously too.

'Don't be silly,' she said, forcing a bright laugh. 'I won't set eyes on him again.'

'I gather you gave him short shrift, then?' Greg guessed, his voice thoughtful.

'Well, what do you think?'

'He may bounce,' Greg warned. 'He looked pretty tough to me. Under that silk shirt there were muscles of steel.'

Greg was joking, but she didn't think it was humorous any more. 'You're scaring me to death,' she said. 'I wouldn't want to find out.'

'You don't fancy him?' Greg spoke lightly but with an undertone of serious question.

'Like rat-poison,' she said tersely.

Greg laughed. 'You're over-stating the case, darling. I'd have said women would find him very collectable.'

'I don't somehow see him on my mantelshelf,' she flipped, but her face wasn't smiling.

Greg paused. 'How hard did he press, Sara?'

He meant the question seriously and she answered it lightly. 'I think you can take it that his intentions were strictly dishonourable.'

'I don't like the idea of you being up there on you own with a wolf prowling round the door.'

'Don't worry, Greg,' she reassured. 'I'm a big girl. I can look after myself, and anyway, I'm unlikely to run into him again. I shall be hard at work from tomorrow and I won't be going into York any more.'

Greg took the hint and dropped the subject. When she had rung off later she sat by the window looking out over the green hills, their smooth surface darkened by the slow passage of the clouds whose shadow moved in the wind's path.

Nick Rawdon had become a shadow on her mind, a darkness troubling her. No man had ever looked at her like that before. It kept coming back, a sudden heat in her veins, a fierce sensation she had never known before. There was no future in a relationship with him, and she had no intention of being lured into one. He would have plenty of other prospects. He probably had a little black book crammed with names and telephone numbers. Even without the glittering allure of his money, he would be irresistible to many women.

She hated admitting it, but she had been slightly tempted herself for a moment. He was a very sexy man and she could imagine that he would be a very exciting lover, but a cold little voice warned her not to start anything with him. They were a million light miles apart. Their life styles clashed, their opinions were irreconcilable. He thought she was a very different proposition than the truth made her. Because of her relationship with Greg, she had become what Greg called 'an easy target' to him, and that really bugged her. She wasn't what he thought and he wasn't getting a thing from her.

Not a thing, she repeated to herself, and was annoyed because she had felt it necessary to repeat it, as though she could ever be tempted into a brief affair with a man she didn't approve of, didn't like. She looked into her mirror later as she got ready for bed and was angry all over again to see the hectic flush on her cheeks, the brightness of her eyes. Damn Nick Rawdon, she thought.

CHAPTER THREE

THE following afternoon she was sitting in front of her easel in a meadow starred with daisies and buttercups, staring up at the hillside, contemplating the deep blue shadow of the stone wall as a wind moved in the boughs of the elm tree beside it. The problem of shadow was worrying her. Her client wanted the hill represented in the early morning, but then the sun hadn't risen and there were no shadows. Her mind moved from the technical problem to another thought. The incredible snaking lengths of stone walls which crawled across hillsides and valleys amazed her. Who had once spent hour upon hour constructing them? They must have been a lifetime's work, and for what? As territorial barriers? Or to keep sheep safely on an owner's land? Even on the open moors where one would least have expected it, one found them. When one considered the time spent on them, Sara thought, they must be at least the Yorkshire equivalent of the Great Pyramid.

It was very hot for the time of year. She was wearing her usual jeans from habit, but she had put on a sun-top, a skimpy little object, without sleeves and with a low scooped neckline, which ended just around her midriff. It gave her more freedom of movement and she enjoyed the circulation of the air on her bare skin. She wished she had put on shorts, too, but she couldn't be bothered to walk back to the Fox and Grapes to change now.

A shadow fell over her shoulder on to the easel and she turned, eyes wide, to look up into Nick Rawdon's face.

Oddly she wasn't even surprised to see him. She looked at him levelly, her face calm.

'What do I have to do to get the message home? Flatten you?'

'You could try,' he said, smiling mockingly.

She turned back to her work. 'Shove off!'

'Charming,' he murmured. 'Just what I'd expected. Your manners are delightful.'

She carefully inched in a fraction of slate-blue shadow on the wall and wondered if the client would remember that there was no shadow at dawn.

It was going to take a long time to finish the wall, anyway. It was a natural perspective builder and already her picture was forming itself around it. She was shutting Nick Rawdon out of her head with an effort. If she ignored him he would go away in the end.

He settled on the grass beside her, his head propped on one hand, his lean body at ease. She knew he was watching her. She knew he was nibbling pensively at a long-stem of meadow grass. She even knew the name of it, identifying the sub-species out of the corner of her eye. She had made a study of grasses at art college. They made an interesting subject and were easy to collect and draw.

'Your lashes are like gold wire,' he commented.

She fluttered them at him, unable to resist the temptation, her sense of humour aroused.

When she had returned to her work, he shifted slightly and began trailing a long piece of grass over her jeans.

'I'm working,' she said, pausing again to glare at him. 'Unlike you, Mr Rawdon, I do have to work or I don't eat. It may be mundane of me, but I like to eat at least once a day.'

'What makes you think I don't work?'

'I'm sure you do,' she shrugged. 'It must be very tiring counting all that money.'

'Why are you so obsessed by my money?'

That stung. 'Who's obsessed? I don't give a damn.'

'You talk about nothing else.'

'I don't want to talk at all,' she said, because it annoyed her to admit he could be right. It was stupid of her to dwell on the subject of his money.

'Neither do I,' he drawled softly with an eye on her profile.

She felt the colour coming up under her skin at the implication, but she tried to concentrate on her work. She was puzzling over how he had got there, how he had known where to look.

'How did you find me?' she asked at last.

'You told me,' he informed her. 'The Fox and Grapes on the Scarborough Road.'

'Simple,' she groaned. 'You ferreted that out of me, didn't you?'

'Mmm,' he agreed. 'Easy as taking candy from a baby, or did you want me to find you?'

She looked at him through her lashes. 'I did not!'

'Sure?'

'Positive,' she said with an edge to her voice.

He moved again, settling himself comfortably, his hands under his head, the long lithe body sheathed in an open dark blue shirt and blue denim trousers. He had dropped a matching jacket on the grass.

She couldn't resist a quick look at him. 'How can I work with you watching me?'

He ostentatiously shut his eyes. 'Who's watching you?'

She went on working, occasionally shooting him a look, but he kept his eyes shut, even the thick black lashes not moving against his hard cheeks. A fat-bodied bumble bee buzzed unsteadily towards him from a patch of clover and hovered around his black head. Sara whispered, 'Don't move. There's a bee near you.'

'I'm not deaf,' he said, eyes still shut.

The bee slowly droned away and Sara sat there, staring at him. My God, she thought, he's good-looking. The sunlight gleamed on his smooth brown skin, was reflected from the thick black hair. His mouth was twitching slightly. Suddenly he lunged and his hand curled round her ankle, pulling her off the stool and into his arms. He received her on his chest, holding her tight.

She had given a yell of surprise, but it turned into laughter, her eyes close to his, seeing the brilliant blue at close quarters with a shock of pleasure.

She lay on top of him, staring into his eyes, and his hand moved softly over her back, stroking the warm sunkissed skin exposed by her brief top.

She ought to be angry, she told herself. This was sheer insanity. How was she going to convince him she wasn't interested if she let him behave like this?

'Doesn't the word no mean anything to you?' she asked.

'Not a lot,' he said with an insolent glance through his black lashes.

He was playing with her hair now, twining his fingers through it, rubbing the soft strands between finger and thumb. 'Your hair looks like marigolds, but it feels like silk. It smells delicious, too.'

'I have to wash it often,' she shrugged. 'It's so fine it drives me mad.'

'It could drive me mad too,' he murmured, the blue gleam of his eyes mocking. 'There are a lot of things about you that could drive me mad.'

'Fight it,' she said, looking at him with teasing eyes, and mentally kicking herself because she should be giving him the frozen glare of offence, not grinning at him like an infatuated idiot.

The trouble was, in his casual denim he looked almost human and the sunlight was giving a dangerous gilding to his undoubted good looks. It was a somnolent, meltingly lovely afternoon, and she was finding the movements of his long hands far too enjoyable.

'Why should I?' he enquired lazily. 'You're quite delectable and I've been waiting for what seems like years to kiss you again.'

He was in no hurry as his hand pulled her head down. She could have jerked away. She could have struggled. She didn't. It was reckless and idiotic, but she would think about the dangers later. Just now she wanted to find out exactly what effect the touch of his mouth would have on her. The first time he kissed her, he had been angry. He had meant to hurt. This time was going to be different, she knew that.

It was earthshaking. His mouth moved lazily, sensually, teasing and playing with her, until it suddenly grew urgent, the hand pressing down on her head taking a grip on her neck to pull her closer, his kiss deepening into a hot, drugging sweetness that was unlike anything she had ever known. She was floating on air, her head empty of everything but a growing physical excitement. His fingers pushed her hair back from her neck and his mouth moved down her cheek to crawl slowly, softly, over every inch of her throat until it was moving on the soft underside of her chin. She had her head tilted back at the command of his hand and she was almost whimpering with pleasure, soft broken little moans breathing through her bruised mouth.

He suddenly rolled, taking her with him, and now she lay on the grass with Nick above her and he was exploring the coiled crevice of her ears, his tongue and lips intimate. Sara made no attempt to protest. She was lying with her eyes wide open, staring at the blue sky, a dazed expression on her face.

He drifted his lips from her ears across her face, touching her skin lightly, taking his time, as though he wanted, needed, to touch and taste every part of her. She sensed that the caresses were deliberately prolonged, a careful seduction, but although her mind still cried out in warning, her body craved what he was doing to her. It was a sensual experience that she could not resist.

The languorous sensations he was arousing held her like a soporific drug. He took her hands, glancing at her with narrowed eyes, and placed them on his chest. 'Touch me, Sara,' he whispered.

It was then she should have drawn back, pushed him away, but she didn't. Her hands flattened on his chest, began undoing his shirt, and he watched her, breathing fast, the lids well down over the glittering blue eyes. The sun poured down over them, bringing the scent of crushed grass to her nostrils. The wind moved lightly in the trees, making them whistle like shocked observers. When her fingers slid over his bare chest Nick groaned pleasurably. 'Yes,' he said. 'Yes.'

Their mouths were suddenly moving hotly against each other although she did not remember him moving. Her hands ran hungrily up his body to clasp his head and Nick pushed his own hands under her brief sun-top to close them over the thrust of her breasts, pausing at the hoarse cry she gave as he touched them.

'You want me. Admit it,' he said thickly.

'Yes,' she said, although the sound was muffled because her lips felt hot and swollen as though passion was altering her cell structure.

'Not now,' he said, as though reluctant to admit that. 'Tonight. Will you come back to my hotel?'

He had lost her in that instant. She stiffened, going cold, because suddenly all the magic went out of the hot afternoon and she remembered what she had forgotten, her mind taking control again, her stupid treacherous body forced back into submission.

She caught him off guard. He had been so certain of her, so triumphant, that he had relaxed and while he was lazily surveying her with the glint of the conqueror, she suddenly pushed him off and sat up before he could recover his balance. She was standing as he slowly got to his feet, staring at her.

Sara reverted to her usual barrier, a flippant little smile on her face.

'Thanks, but no, thanks, Mr Rawdon,' she drawled lightly. 'It's a tempting prospect, of course, but Greg wouldn't like it.'

The lazy amusement had gone out of his face. He was looking at her with savage anger, his eyes biting.

'You changed your mind pretty quickly.'

'I didn't change a thing,' she tossed, her chin up.

'Oh, yes,' he said between his teeth. 'That wasn't play-acting. I had you and you know it.'

'You'll never have me, Mr Rawdon,' she said furiously, feeling her face burning.

He pushed his hands into his pockets, his black head angrily set. 'We'll see about that.'

'Do you want it in writing? I'm not on offer.'

He moved closer, his eyes glittering between the heavy lids. 'Halliday need never know, if that's what's bothering you.'

Her flush deepened. She couldn't now repeat that she and Greg were not lovers. For her own protection he had to believe they were or she would be under siege until she gave in to him.

'What a charming suggestion,' she said instead contemptuously. 'You think I'm that despicable?'

'I think you want me as much as I want you,' he told her with his blue eyes burning on her face.

'No!'

'Don't lie to me. I could have taken you just now without a struggle—you admitted it yourself. You said yes. You know damned well you did.'

'You have no scruples about taking a woman from the man you believe she loves?' The scornful flick of her eyes made him look angry, his face toughening into a hard mask.

'I'd take you from my own brother,' he said, and

he meant it. 'I don't give a damn how I get you so long as I do.'

She looked at him in appalled understanding, suddenly seeing the forceful tenacious lines of his face in a new light. He would stop at nothing, she thought. He was a total bastard.

'I can see you make a great banker,' she told him icily. 'I wouldn't borrow a bent pin from you. Your interest rates are prohibitive.'

'Make up your mind to it, Sara,' he merely said harshly. 'I want you and I'm going to have you. I wanted you the moment I set eyes on you.' He moved his shoulders as though arming himself for a long struggle, his mouth tautly determined. 'Anyone in the City will tell you that I always reach my objective.'

'Get lost,' she said, suddenly frightened. 'I never want to set eyes on you again!'

'That's too bad,' Nick shrugged. 'Because I'll be back.' He bent and picked up his jacket, slung it over one shoulder, the lean graceful lines of his body making her heart miss a beat. Anger at her own weakness gave a sharpness to her voice.

'I expect Greg any day now.'

He looked at her levelly, a cold smile on his mouth. 'Going to ring him and have him running up here to fend me off, are you?'

She lied. 'He was coming anyway.'

Nick didn't believe her, of course. He shook his black head, the hard mouth amused. 'Try again, Sara. I know a fairy tale when I hear it. It makes no difference, anyway. A dozen Greg Hallidays wouldn't stop me.'

She looked into his face with a terrified belief that it was true. His face was impervious, dressed in steely authority. The blue eyes held menace, certainty, immovable willpower.

'Not even knowing that I love him?' she asked as a last resort.

She saw his face change. 'So he is your lover? You admit that now?'

She silently nodded, swallowing.

'Why lie, then? Do you think I didn't notice the way you couldn't take your eyes off him at that party?'

'It was none of your business,' she said huskily.

He stared at her, his eyes searching her flushed face, his mouth straight and angry.

'At least we've got the truth now,' he said with a cold intonation. 'I prefer to know where I stand. Why don't you marry him?'

'Greg doesn't believe in marriage,' she managed to say, although the strain of standing here lying was making her feel miserable and sick. She wondered how she was going to explain all this to Greg. He wouldn't be very pleased when he knew the lie she had saddled him with, but what other option had she had?

'Do you?' Nick asked tersely.

She couldn't quite meet his eyes. 'No,' she said feebly, aware that her evasion was glaringly apparent.

'You don't sound very certain about that,' he said

with a cool derision. 'Won't he make an honest woman of you, is that it?'

'Greg loves me,' she said, and that was true, so she could lift her head and look him straight in the eyes again.

'Not very much, it seems.'

'You swine,' she whispered shakily.

His mouth twisted. 'Sorry if the truth hurts.'

'You wouldn't know the truth if it came up and bit you.'

'It seems I know a lot more about it than you do. At least I was honest about my intentions. You lied to me about Halliday. I knew you lied, but that doesn't let you off the hook. Lie about one thing and you'll lie about another. You're lying when you say you don't want me, and one day I'll make you admit that, too.' He looked at her as he finished speaking, then he turned and walked away across the sunlit grass.

Sara debated, of course, whether to ring Greg or not, but the thought of asking him to drive all the way up to Yorkshire to fend off Nick Rawdon for her was so embarrassing that she decided she couldn't do it. Some instinct told her that Nick wouldn't be back this time. There had been a chill light in those blue eyes before he turned and walked away.

She turned out to be right. Nick did not show up again during her time in Yorkshire. She painted steadily without further interruption, but although her days were tranquil and unbroken, her nights were not. She couldn't sleep. She turned over and over like a restless dog in a new house, fighting to stop her treacherous mind from dwelling on things she preferred to ignore.

How seriously had he meant his threat to her peace of mind? He had shown her a passion she had never seen before, but he had changed when she brought Greg into the picture. Had her admission that she loved Greg driven him away?

It was what she wanted. She reminded herself of that again and again. She wasn't going to be stupid enough to let a reckless mood sweep her into an affair with Nick Rawdon. She had always hated reading a book to which she knew the ending, and every instinct she possessed warned her precisely what end there would be to any relationship with Nick.

At their first meeting she had only been aware of him as a dark, hostile presence, and that hostility had been present again when he came to her house next day. It had vanished during her lunch with him in his suite. Somehow, without her meaning to let it happen, she had felt a precarious growth between them; a slow, subtle development rather like the putting down of roots in the dark which took place each spring. These roots of feeling were tentative as yet. Pale, fragile threads groping from one to the other and easily snapped at present. Perhaps they had been snapped by what happened in the meadow; Sara wasn't certain about that. The silent, heated passion they had exchanged was something else. She had been mindless as she lay in his arms, but she was intelligent enough to know that her reactions to him had not been based on emotion. Nick had touched a spring of desire in her, but it had been purely physical, something quite apart from the hesitant, delicate stirring of feeling which had been going on at the same time.

She had always felt that love, when it happened to her, would combine the two, but she did not want them to flower for Nick Rawdon. That could only be disastrous for her.

As day followed day and there was no sign of him, she told herself how glad she was, but she found herself hard to convince. She persuaded herself that he had entirely passed out of her mind, but when the slate blue shadows thickened on the stone walls she found herself thinking of his blue eyes darkening with passion, and when she went into York to get some more paints she found herself looking over her shoulder all the time.

Her picture did not suffer, however. Her mental turmoil did not seem to harm her capacity, indeed she felt vaguely that she had somehow acquired a new depth. Certainly, the client was delighted. Sara had painted his hillside with a loving perception which brought a beam to his face. She hated handing it over to him. Although she would not face the fact, she had painted into the canvas something of the feelings she had experienced in the meadow that day. The green hillside, the trees, the spilling shadows, were permeated with memories for her now, and it showed. How could she keep it out? The client, of course, was blithely unaware of any hidden depths. He looked at the landscape and he saw what he had always seen and was contented.

She drove back to London and Greg looked sharply at her as she walked into the house. He didn't say anything, but Sara felt oddly conspicuous, as though what was happening inside her was written in letters ten feet high on her face.

Greg was observant. He knew her very well. And he missed very little with those melancholy brown eyes.

They had dinner with Lucy and Rob the following night. Lucy had gone to town on the meal and the food was so superb that Sara sat back after dinner, sighing, 'I shall have to diet for a week now!'

'You need some flesh,' said Rob, eyeing her. 'When you arrived I thought you were a stick insect in those trousers.'

She fluttered her lashes coyly at him. 'I've been told I look very sexy in them.' That was true. The black trouser suit was made of a crêpe material which lovingly followed every curve of her body, the tiny tunic fringed with black and silver threads.

'Who by?' Rob enquired.

She threw him a grin. 'Men.'

'My God!' exclaimed Rob, miming horror. 'You be careful. You never know what could come of that.'

'Oh, I've a shrewd idea,' she retorted, leaning back in her chair, her hands linked behind her bright head, the stretch of her body very feminine.

'Depraved hussy,' he murmured, eyeing her with exaggerated interest. She moved a hand to pat his cheek, smiling wickedly at him, and he put up his own hand to catch her wrist clumsily. His hands had once been graceful, clever. It hurt to see their ungainly movements now, but Sara gave him a brilliant smile.

'Lucy, your husband's making advances to me!'

Lucy looked through the hatch to the kitchen, where she was making coffee with Greg, and scolded indulgently, 'Hands off, Rob, you disgusting man. Can't you leave the girl alone?'

'She brings out the beast in me,' Rob retorted with a mock growl and a leer.

'Not only in you,' Greg said through the hatch. 'She's had a rich merchant banker prowling around her lately.'

Sara flushed hotly and looked round at him, her eyes requesting him to drop the subject. Greg caught the glance and his brows lifted sharply. But Rob was intrigued, delighted to hear some amusing gossip.

He leaned forward in his chair, the blurred lines of his once attractive face a painful reminder of his illness, and looking at his sparkling eyes, Sara did not have the heart to stop him.

'What's this? What's this? Do I scent intrigue?'

Sara met Greg's eyes and he read her silent permission to answer.

'Remember I took her to a party a few weeks back? She met up with Nick Rawdon and he flipped his lid over her.'

Scalding colour rushed into her face. 'I didn't say that,' she protested.

'Rawdon,' Rob mused aloud, his swollen fingers

on his knees. 'That would be Rawdon's Bank—an old City institution. I know the building well—one of the pleasures of London, Lazreth Square.' He sighed, his face altering, and Greg watched him with a taut smile. They all knew what Rob was thinking. He had barely left this house for months. Then Rob thrust that look from his face and smiled brightly. 'A beautiful Georgian square. Rawdons have a corner terraced house, five storeys of it, with styled ironwork balconies and the usual elegant façade. White steps going up to the front door, a polished-brass door plate, iron railings around the basement.' He had his eyes wide open, but mentally Sara knew he was seeing that house, that quiet London square.

Lucy stood at Greg's shoulder, watching her husband. She was a slight, delicate woman with dark hair and eyes, and she had learnt to smile without showing a thing on her face. Now her features were quite empty, but Sara caught sight of her hands. They were twisting a tea towel in a jerky, convulsive way which wrung Sara's heart.

Rob glanced at Sara. 'You ought to get your banker admirer to take you round the place. Well worth seeing, I'd say. It isn't often you get the chance to see a building still being used for the purpose for which it was designed. The bank have occupied that house since the early years of the nineteenth century.'

'I doubt if I'll ever see him again,' Sara said with an almost pious sigh.

'That prayer came from the heart,' Rob observed,

watching her. 'Do you hope not or the opposite?'

She laughed, looking flushed and uncertain. 'Greg was exaggerating, as usual. It was nothing.'

Greg pointed out to Lucy that the coffee was ready and somehow the topic was dropped. Driving back to their home, later, Greg glanced at Sara hesitantly and said: 'I'm sorry I brought Rawdon up.'

'It doesn't matter.'

'I think it does,' said Greg. 'Did he get to you, Sara?'

Her cheeks bloomed instantly and she stammered, 'What on earth do you mean?'

He stared ahead at the dark road, the yellow pools of light from the street lamps flashing past as he drove. 'Something happened up in Yorkshire. You were different when you came back.'

'It wasn't that,' she retorted.

Greg grimaced. 'I wasn't prying.'

'There's nothing to pry into,' she insisted. 'I met him twice up there and nothing happened.'

It was a lie—she knew it as she said it. Something had happened, all right, but she wasn't sure what. Whatever it was, was still so fragile and buried so deep inside her own mind that she hesitated to dig it up to inspect it. As she had said, she wasn't likely to see Nick again and gradually that tentative feeling would perish from sheer lack of air.

Greg respected her need for privacy just as he expected her to respect his, but he wasn't blind to the change in her and he had given her the opportunity to confide in him if she wished. Now that she had quietly turned it down, Greg wouldn't probe any deeper, and she was grateful to him for his delicacy. She did not want to talk about Nick Rawdon; she didn't even want to think about him.

That was harder than she had expected, though. As the weeks went by he kept intruding into her mind without warning. During the day she was able to keep herself so occupied that she could hurriedly turn off whenever a thought of him occurred, but at night it was much harder. She would lie in the darkness, her busy brain spawning images that left her breathless. No man had ever aroused her in the way he had. He was like some sudden fever which had deposited a germ in her blood so that from time to time it came to life once more, travelling dangerously through her veins.

It was two months later that she and Greg walked into a London art dealer's gallery to seen an exhibition being given by a friend of Greg's. Sara was sparkling as she talked to the very tall, thin man who was exhibiting. He had always flirted with her when they met and he did so now, teasingly, his light eyes not serious. He was excited about his exhibition and not displeased to have Sara smiling at him as he talked to her, but neither of them meant anything much by their gay exchange of banter.

She was wearing her silvery dress, the light flashing off it as she stood there, her green eyes dancing with amusement as she listened. Greg came up behind her and slid his arms around her waist, leaning his chin on her shoulder.

'What are you two up to? Can't I leave you alone for a minute, girl?'

His friend grinned. 'She's far too beautiful to be left unattended,' he retorted.

Sara glanced sideways and Greg's brown eyes met hers, a comical wryness in his face. 'You're keeping the man from his eager public,' he told her.

'Nothing of the kind,' he was told by his friend. 'Clear off, Greg. We were doing very well without you.'

'Perhaps you should be circulating,' said Sara, wondering exactly why Greg had interrupted. It wasn't like him to behave like a dog in the manger, but she knew him well enough to take the hint he had given her.

His friend bowed regretfully, kissing her hand, and moved off, humming the tune *Jealousy* in a meaningful way. Greg smiled, but with his cheek still against hers he murmured, 'Rawdon is here.'

Sara stiffened. 'That's why you came over.'

'I thought you ought to know. He's been watching you for the past ten minutes.'

She felt her eyes beginning to wander and Greg straightened and moved in front of her, blocking her view of the room. She looked up into his face enquiringly.

'There's no need for high drama, Greg. He won't pounce on me like a ravenous tiger.'

Greg had a faint frown. 'You didn't see yourself when you got back from Yorkshire. I've no wish to see you look like that again.'

She felt herself colouring. Greg watched her and she couldn't quite meet his eyes.

'He's poison to you,' he commented.

She took his hand, holding it tightly. 'Greg, there's something I ought to tell you. I told him we were lovers.'

Greg's brown eyes opened wide and then narrowed into dark slits, watching her. 'Now why should you do that? Don't tell me, let me guess.'

'You're angry—I guessed you would be. I'm sorry, Greg. I had no business lying about you and I'm sorry to have embarrassed you.'

'Don't be absurd,' Greg said flatly. 'It doesn't bother me, except that it shows me how close he was hunting. You wouldn't have made up such a story unless you had good reason.'

Her colour deepened. She nodded, staring at the floor.

Greg suddenly put a hand around her head and bent to kiss her lightly. 'Don't worry, baby. I'll keep him away.' His grin broke across his sad-funny face. 'You've played bodyguard for me before now.'

Behind his shoulder Sara caught an advancing face and with a stifled giggle said, 'You're going to need one now, too.'

She saw the alarm flash into his eyes, but before he could move Lorna Roberts was embracing him, kissing his cheek. 'Greg darling!'

'Hallo, Lorna,' he said in resigned tones. He gently detached himself and caught Sara's hand in a casual manner. 'Enjoying Peter's exhibition?'

Lorna ignored Sara, her thin dark face hungry as she looked at Greg. She was a volatile woman with incredible persistence and Greg had never found it in his heart to snub her so unmercifully that she would take the message. His polite evasions did him no good. Lorna pursued him without ever seeming to notice that he showed no returning interest.

'I think I've got you a client,' she said now. She was indefatigable about chasing up business for him, but even that could not lessen Greg's weary resistance to her. He held on to Sara as Lorna steered him towards a small group standing some way across the room.

'Now, be charming to them, Greg,' Lorna chided him.

He gave Sara a wry little smile sideways, but she wasn't looking at him. She was staring at the man facing her in the little group and he was staring back.

Greg's hand tightened on her as he saw Nick, but then Lorna was introducing them and there was a polite little gabble from the other members of the group. Somehow Lorna contrived to separate Sara from Greg and somehow Nick was beside her, and she looked up into his blue eyes with a sensation of total helplessness.

He put his hand under her elbow and she let him move her away from the group. Her heart was thudding in a sickening way and her eyes were too brilliant.

He looked at her through those heavy, cynical lids and she felt feverish as she looked back.

'I wondered if you would be here,' he drawled.

'Peter's a friend of Greg's.' Was that her voice? She didn't recognise it. It sounded too high, too unstable.

The hard mouth twisted. 'Is he? I had the impression he fancied you.'

She looked at him quickly. He had been watching her and Peter talking and God knows what he had been thinking. She had been flirting cheerfully, unaware of being watched, and now her cheeks burnt as she met his eyes.

'What are you doing here?' she asked him self-defensively. 'I didn't think you were a patron of the arts.'

'I'm here in case I might see you,' he said, and the frank reply threw her. She could only look at him with her mouth open like a stupid fish out of water and he started to grin suddenly.

'Catching flies?'

She shut her mouth.

'Have dinner with me,' he said, moving closer, his blue eyes on her face.

Sara shook her head, not daring to trust her voice. His hand slid up her bare arm and she shivered at the touch. She wanted to say yes. At this moment she knew she ached to be alone with him. That wasn't all she wanted, but she wouldn't think of that. The art dealer giving the exhibition was circulating with a tray. He paused beside them, giving Nick an interested, respectful look, and grinned at Sara.

'Hallo, Gerry,' she said, taking a glass of his champagne.

'That's all you're getting tonight,' he warned. 'I'm not made of money.'

She had known him for quite a while. She knew his passion for little economies and she merely made a face at him as she sipped from the glass.

Gerry gave Nick another of his respectful smiles and she realised he knew who Nick was and was hoping he had found a new client.

Nick took a glass and then gave Gerry a look. It wasn't exactly menacing, but Gerry swallowed and vanished.

Sara couldn't help giggling. Gerry was soft-skinned, timid, a little malicious. He would no doubt find Nick alarming.

'A good trick, that,' she said, sipping more champagne and finding it was lessening his effect on her. She felt brave and lighthearted suddenly. She gave Nick a teasing little smile. 'What do you do for an encore?'

'Guess,' he said, moving closer, looking at her in an unmistakable fashion.

She moved her head back, her green eyes glinting. 'I wouldn't like to come and ask you for a loan. You must be terrifying behind a desk.'

'Oh, I think you'd get a sympathetic hearing,' he drawled, his smile needing no explanation.

She fluttered her lashes at him. 'Would I? No collateral?'

'I didn't say that,' he drawled, glancing down at her warm curved body.

Greg moved beside them suddenly and Nick turned his black head to stare coldly at him. Greg stared back, his thin melancholy features filled with hostility.

'Coming to look at the pictures, Sara?' Greg asked her.

'We're talking,' Nick said between his teeth, and suddenly his whole face changed. He looked at Greg with the eyes of someone who is only waiting for the chance to hit out, a barely controlled violence in his face. Sara felt her heart come up into her mouth. It had never occurred to her that he might make a scene here in public, but suddenly she was afraid he would. He had a reckless glitter in his eyes, his body poised on the edge of movement.

'Would you mind if I had dinner with Nick, Greg?' she asked to stop him, and both men swivelled their heads to stare at her. Greg looked incredulous. Nick had a narrowed stare.

Greg held her eyes, his face irritated. 'I can't stop you,' he said tersely. That wasn't all he said, but the rest was silent, his eyes asking her what the hell she thought she was playing at, asking her if she was out of her skull.

Nick took her glass out of her hand and put it down beside his on a convenient ledge. He put a hand under her arm and without a word to Greg he steered her out of the gallery, leaving Greg staring after them.

CHAPTER FOUR

'WHAT changed your mind?' he asked as they walked along the pavement in the cool night air. The wind blew a scrap of paper past them and she watched it rustling past shop windows until it vanished into the dark.

'Can't I change my mind without giving reasons?'

He steered her towards a long silver-grey car which was parked at the kerb. 'I don't give a damn why you're coming with me so long as you are,' he said, opening the car and helping her into the passenger seat. He walked round and climbed in beside her, his hands on the steering wheel. He gave her a brief glance from under his black lashes.

'What's Halliday going to make of it, though?'

She blushed and shrugged. 'I'm a free individual.'

'Yes?' His dark brows rose crookedly. 'I didn't get that impression just now. He came hurrying over to separate us, didn't he? He made no bones about it —I recognised the look he gave me. But you dug your heels in suddenly. Why?' He watched her closely, his face hard. 'Are you using me, Sara?'

She stared. 'Using you?'

'To make him jealous?'

She gave a brief laugh. 'That hadn't occurred to me.'

'No? I wonder.' He started the ignition and the

car engine idled purringly. 'I won't like it if you are,' he said, looking in his wing mirror before he slid out into the street. 'I give you fair warning.'

She leaned back in her seat, her hands in her lap. 'Where are we going?'

'You'll see,' he returned softly.

'How very mysterious!' He looked like a stranger, his long hands on the wheel, his harsh profile capped by the thick black hair. The light from passing street lamps brought out a few silver hairs in it, giving his face a new distinction. I barely know him, Sara thought. Am I crazy doing this?

He pulled off into an underground car-park and she looked round in distrust at the echoing concrete caverns, their shadows only dimly lit. Nick came round and helped her out, guiding her towards a lift nearby.

'Where are we?' she asked, her feet dragging a little as he led her through the darkness.

He opened the lift door and she found herself shepherded into it. The door closed and the lift began to ascend. 'Where are we?' she asked again. He leaned on the grey metallic wall and eyed her, a little smile on the hard mouth.

'Almost there,' he said softly.

She felt a tremor of fever running through her veins. Her colour deepened and the green eyes flashed brilliantly at him.

'I don't trust you,' she heard herself saying.

He smiled slowly, his black head bent to survey her. 'No?' His hand brushed her hot cheek, then he

turned as the lift slowed to a halt and the door slid
open.

The corridor into which she stepped was thickly
carpeted in a dark blue. Her pulses drummed as
she stood there mulishly, facing him with her bright
head held high. 'This is your flat, isn't it?'

He smiled but said nothing, watching her with a
derisive sparkle in the blue eyes.

'Do you think I'm an idiot? I'm not going to your
flat at this hour of the night!'

He touched the small button on the wall by the
door, his eyes still amused, and Sara turned on her
heel to walk back into the lift. He stretched out a
lazy arm and caught her back, holding her easily as
she struggled to get away.

She was still fighting him when the door began to
open. Sara stopped to stare as a short, grey-haired
woman appeared, giving Nick a smile. 'Oh, good
evening, sir. I wondered who it was at this hour.'

Very flushed, Sara wondered what on earth to do,
not liking the idea of bolting again while this
sensible-looking woman watched in amazement.

Nick deftly guided her into the long hall, his
hands removing her short fur jacket. 'We'll have
dinner, Mrs Firth,' he said casually, over his shoulder, tossing Sara's jacket to the woman.

'Yes, sir,' the woman said without surprise.

Nick was already opening a door and ushering
Sara through it. She paused to stare around her,
taking in the enormous room with fascination. It
was decorated in muted shades of grey and blue, the
whole effect being tranquil and unobtrusive, the

furniture very modern, all squares and blocks, yet deeply padded and ultra-comfortable.

She had already realised that this was the penthouse suite in the building. There had only been one door in that long corridor outside, so presumably Nick had the whole floor to himself. The size of this room was impressive, but it could only take up a fifth of the floor space available to him. Presumably there were a number of bedrooms further down the corridor.

'Drink?' he asked, moving to a fluted glass wall whose smoked grey surface reflected the soft light of a pale blue lamp beside it. Sara watched with interest as the glass slid back silently at a touch to reveal a well-stocked array of bottles. Nick glanced over his shoulder at her, eyebrows raised. 'What would you like?'

'A dry Martini,' she said, wandering around the room. She paused in front of the vast grey couch covered in blue velvet cushions, eyeing it distrustfully.

Nick put a glass into her hand, grinning. 'You have a transparent mind, my love.'

She lifted her green eyes to his face. 'So have you,' she threw back.

'Then we understand each other,' he drawled, his mouth twisting.

She glanced round the room. 'Are the lights always this low?'

There was a sardonic gleam in his eye. 'When I'm entertaining they are,' he told her.

'And I'm sure you do a lot of that,' she said, feeling a peculiar sharp twist inside her. How many other women had he had up here? Was there a different girl each night? Or did he have a few regular visitors?

He was watching her with an expressionless face and she hoped he couldn't read on her face what was going on inside her head.

'How many rooms are there?' she asked to change the subject.

'Seven plus the servants' quarters,' he shrugged. He moved to a door, opened it. 'Dining-room,' he said, and she looked past his shoulder into the smaller room which was as muted but all decorated in shades of soft apricot and amber, the effect warm and relaxing. 'I've a study through there,' Nick pointed. 'And then there are the four bedrooms.' His black lashes stirred against his cheek as he gave her an oblique little smile. 'Would you like to see them now?'

She turned away quickly. 'No, thank you.' What did he mean 'now'? He could think again. Thank heavens he had servants on the premises. She was very relieved to know that.

Her eye was caught by a line of silver-framed photographs and she paused to look at them. 'My family,' Nick told her, standing at her shoulder.

She was intrigued. 'Tell me who they are,' she demanded.

He pointed. 'My sister, Judith.' Sara studied the face with its charming but posed smile, a frame of smooth black hair curled round it, eyes which held

Nick's assertive strength and a firm straight mouth.

'Is she younger than you?'

'By two years,' he admitted.

'Married?' There was no man in the photograph, yet somehow Judith looked married, she had a contented look as though her life pleased her.

'Indelibly,' Nick said drily.

'What does that mean?'

'In Judith's case, four children and an obsession with education at present.'

'Are you a doting uncle?' She couldn't believe that and the question was a deliberate tease. Nick knew it and his glance was menacing.

'I'm a reluctant one,' he admitted. 'The eldest three are boys in whom Judith imagines I must be fascinated. In fact, they bore me to tears. The youngest is a girl they've stupidly named Nicola and she has a pronounced squint, no teeth and very little hair. Judith supposes that she flatters me by telling me the child looks like me.'

Sara laughed. 'It sounds as if she does!'

His blue eyes held laughter. 'I'll remember that.'

She backed slightly, smiling. 'How old is Nicola?'

'Six weeks,' he returned drily. 'Judith assures me she's going to be beautiful.'

'Then perhaps she's not so like you,' Sara said softly, grinning at him.

He took a step towards her and she turned away, breathless. 'What exactly does a banker do?' she asked him as she walked across the room.

He caught her as she neared the couch and twisted her deftly down on to it. 'I've had enough polite conversation,' he said as he leaned towards her.

Her heart was racing so fast she wondered if he could hear it. His mouth swooped down in predatory hunger and Sara lost all sense of what she was doing. The thick warm darkness into which she fell had neither time nor place. When at last he pulled back and she surfaced again her arms were clinging round his neck and she was conscious of having totally lost her cool.

Nick's blue eyes were very close, a glitter in them. 'Yes,' he whispered, as if she had said something.

She forced herself away from him and he let her go, but he watched her with a smile that was like a knife.

To her amazement he suddenly began to talk about his work. He made banking sound quite fascinating, talking of international investments, personal loans, the day-by-day movements of money.

'I'm told you have a very beautiful building,' she said.

'Yes, it is much admired,' he agreed. 'You must come and see it.'

'I'd like to,' she said.

'When?' he asked, and she looked at him in surprise, because she saw he meant the question, he wanted to fix a day and time, and then she saw something else, a restless gleam in his eyes as he looked at her.

'When will you come?' he asked when she didn't answer him. 'On Monday? I'll take you round myself.'

Her throat felt hot because she knew he was nailing her down to a promise to see him again. Nick was going to try to drag her into a relationship. To-night was only the beginning.

'Monday?' he pressed again. 'Monday afternoon would be easiest for me. I've a working conference every Monday morning.'

'I'm afraid I'm busy on Monday afternoon,' she lied.

His eyes narrowed. 'Tuesday, then,' he said.

'I'll have to let you know,' she excused weakly.

Then Mrs Firth came in to announce that dinner was ready and they moved into the smooth bland dining-room and ate the perfectly cooked meal, seated opposite each other at the deep-polished oval dining table, the glow of candles reflected in the wood and a scent of carnations giving the air a spicy sweetness. They were eating chicken in a vinous white sauce and drinking a chilled German wine with it, the light flickering in the pale straw-coloured liquid as she lifted her glass. Across the table Nick watched her, the arrogant face unread-able. They talked about music, argued about com-posers. Nick refilled her glass and Mrs Firth came in with a whipped sweet rich with raspberries. After that they had coffee and brandy in the muted light of the grey-blue room and Nick played her a new recording he had just bought, a Schubert recital, the lyrical notes rippling through the room while they sat and listened.

Her head was cloudy, thoughtless, and she leaned back on the soft cushions waiting.

She knew and Nick knew that when the music

ended he would take her in his arms, and she was trembling slightly as the last notes fell to silence.

The wine and brandy had dissolved all her inhibitions, removed the restraint of common sense. The need Nick had bred in her that day in the sunlit meadow was now dominant. He turned and looked down at her, his eyes restless.

'You're so beautiful,' he said softly. 'Do you know that? The moment I set eyes on you I knew I had to have you.'

Once she would have run like a rabbit from such a statement. Now she merely gazed at him blindly, waiting, her green eyes fixed on his hard, sensual mouth.

It slowly moved down towards her own and her eyes closed, her arms going round his neck, a long sigh of pleasure on her lips.

His kiss was urgent from the beginning, a demanding heat in the movement of his mouth, a flaring hunger which she knew she felt herself and to which she gave back hunger, lying in his arms without resistance, weak and yielding, her hands stroking his thick black hair.

His hands travelled softly down her body and she moaned, moving closer to him. He slid a hand under her and she felt her zip smoothly glide down. He gently drew the silvery gauze away from her shoulders and put his lips against the fine bones beneath the creamy skin. As his mouth travelled lower she felt the urgency growing inside them both. He was breathing hard, murmuring something she didn't even hear, and she was gasping with pleasure, her eyes shut tight.

He pushed her down among the cushions and the silver gauze fell completely away. She shivered slightly, trembling, but nothing would wake her now from the trance of aroused desire in which he had her.

'Sara,' he muttered hoarsely, the black head moving against her body. 'Oh, God, you're beautiful!'

His hands were warm on her naked skin, but she felt her teeth chattering slightly and tried to stop them, but the excitement she was trapped in was making her almost shocked. She couldn't stop shaking. She moved nearer to him for warmth and his mouth found her own again, taking it in a possessive movement. 'I want you,' he whispered on her lips, and the tremor ran through her whole body.

She felt his hands moving again, but now he was undressing himself. The firm warm nakedness of his chest on her made her open her eyes briefly. He looked at her, sensing the movement, and she was shattered by the feverish brilliance of his eyes.

His heart was pounding down on her and there was a fine dew of perspiration on his forehead. His face had a dark, hot colour which she could feel as well as see. The heat was burning in him.

'Love me,' he groaned with his eyes on her mouth. 'Love me, darling.'

She almost winced at the burning sensation which his voice ignited in her flesh. She was melting heatedly, gasping, moving restlessly beneath him, their bodies pressed closer and closer.

The sudden sharp eruption of the telephone was such a shock that she gave a cry of panic. Nick lifted his black head, the tumbled hair twisted by her caressing hands into strange peaks, and swore.

He looked down at her, grimacing. 'I'll have to answer that or Mrs Firth will come wandering in,' he said, getting up.

He spoke curtly into the receiver. Sara sat up, shivering, to look at him, all her excited heat draining away. She saw Nick's face change, saw the hard rage which filled his eyes.

Wordlessly he flung the telephone down and turned. 'Halliday,' he said through his teeth.

She hurried to the phone and asked huskily, 'Greg?'

'Sara, it's Rob,' he said in a deep voice that held a terrible grief.

She went white, her colour vanishing. 'Oh, Greg ...'

'Can you come now? Lucy is in a state of collapse and I can't do a thing.'

He wouldn't dare be alone with Lucy for long or he might lose control, Sara realised. Lucy would be distraught, grief-stricken, and Greg would be so unhappy for her that he might somehow do or say something to give her a clue to his feelings.

'Greg, is it ...' She paused, unable to ask. 'Are you saying it's all over?'

'Yes,' he said briefly, agonised.

'Greg darling ...'

'Come now, Sara. She needs you. I can't bear to see her.'

'I'm coming now,' she said, tears in her eyes. 'Please, Greg, try to bear it.' Words were so inadequate, so stupid. Men had invented them as instruments of communication and when it really mattered, they failed. At times like these words could do nothing. Human beings relied instead upon looks, touches, unformed murmurs.

She had totally forgotten Nick in the shock of hearing of Rob's death. She put down the phone and turned to find her clothes, her face distracted, pale.

Nick had dressed and was standing by the couch, a glass in his hand, staring at the whisky in it with a face in which nothing showed.

'I've got to go,' she said miserably, picking up her dress. The silver folds slid over her head and she slid into her shoes, her red-gold hair tangled and confused after their lovemaking.

'He whistles and you come,' Nick said to his glass.

She looked at him, opened her mouth to explain and then on instinct closed it. What could she say? She had almost committed an act of monumental folly and it was best just to go.

'Could you get me a taxi?' she asked nervously.

'I'll drive you,' said Nick. He spoke each word as though he hated the taste of them in his mouth and his face was savage. 'What did he do? Threatened to leave you, did he? Said it was all over if you didn't come hurrying back to him?'

He had misread the conversation, she realised, but maybe that was all for the best.

'Please, could we go?' she asked in a stiff little voice. 'I'm in a hurry.'

'Of course,' he said, swallowing the whisky. The glass hit the table with a crash and he stalked to the door. Sara followed in his wake, looking at his black head with bitter resignation.

In the luxurious silver-grey car he said sarcastically, 'How lucky we didn't fix a date for you to see the bank.'

She looked at her hands without answering, her head bent.

'You little bitch,' he muttered. 'If you love him like this, why were you in my arms just now?' His hand clamped down on her arm, wrenching it. She gave a little cry of pain and looked up, finding the blue eyes unrecognisable in their burning anger.

'Answer me. Why were you going to let me make love to you? You were, weren't you? You can't deny that. Ten minutes more and we'd have been in bed. So why? Do you do this all the time? Is that it? Is he used to it? Is that why he won't marry you?'

She pulled her arm out of his savage grip, nursing it angrily. 'Go to hell!' she snapped.

'Thank you,' Nick muttered. 'Maybe I will.'

He started the car and roared out without even looking where he was going, almost colliding with another car as they shot out of the underground car-park. A horn blared angrily and Nick ignored it, driving like a madman, his face a black mask across which the yellow lamplight flashed now and then, illuminating eyes which had a deep fiery rage in them and a mouth which was straight and bitter.

He drove her back to her house. When the car ground to a halt with a squeal she opened the door and got out. She had barely taken two steps when the car roared away again. She looked after the vanishing tail lights, feeling sick. She would never see him again; she was certain of that.

She turned and hurried down the road to Lucy's house, her heels clicking metallically on the pavement. A cat ran across the road and she jumped, shivering. There were lights on in the lower storey and as she went up the path Greg opened the door and silently stood back to let her pass.

She looked at him sharply, seeing everything, knowing him so well that she saw what Greg made certain nobody else ever saw.

He gestured to the sitting-room and Sara went in there. Lucy sat in a chair, very upright, looking white and shocked, her lower lip grazed and wearing spots of blood as though she had been biting it for a long time.

Sara went to her and put her arms around her, holding her, but Lucy didn't cry until Sara herself sobbed abruptly, unable to hold it back, and then Lucy began to cry in a way which Sara found so unbearable that she cried too.

Greg closed the door on them and walked away.

An hour later, Lucy let Sara put her to bed and lay like a child in between the sheets, her black hair straying loose over the pillow. Sara had got her to drink some warm milk into which she had secretly placed a sleeping pill the doctor had given her. Lucy said quietly, 'It was so quick. I hadn't expected it— that's what I can't bear. There was no time any more.'

Sara picked up her hairbrush and brushed her hair gently, winding the strands round her fingers. Lucy talked a little, her voice growing slower and sleepier, and then at last her eyes closed and Sara stopped brushing her hair and clicked off the light.

She found Greg in the kitchen playing a slow game of patience with a pack of very old cards. He looked up at her and she came over to kiss his forehead lightly.

'It was his heart in the end,' Greg said. 'Just stopped.'

'Have you had anything to drink? Shall I make you some coffee or cocoa?'

'Cocoa,' said Greg, shuffling his cards back together.

He watched her go over and light the gas under a saucepan of milk. 'What did I interrupt, Sara?' he asked flatly. 'Rawdon sounded berserk.'

'Nothing,' she said. 'Not a thing.' Nothing that mattered, she thought. He might have saved her from a great deal of grief because Nick was right, of course. If Greg hadn't rung she would have been in bed with him by now. She hadn't even thought of evading him. She had been giving herself without restraint and now she was sick with disgust at her own stupidity. If she had drifted into an affair with him she would have got hurt in the end because Nick Rawdon didn't belong in her world and she didn't belong in his. The expensive trappings of luxury in his penthouse should have stopped her from making a fool of herself, but they hadn't. She had been besottedly eager to let him have whatever he wanted, and he would have taken everything he could.

'Sure?' Greg asked, and she looked round, surprised by his presence because she had forgotten him for a moment.

She gave him a bitter smile. 'Oh, I'm sure. I'm glad you rang.'

'I despise myself,' Greg said sombrely. 'I couldn't do a thing because she hadn't cried and I knew if she did I might go to pieces, so I had to send for you. I'm a coward, a weak fool.' He crashed his hand down and the cards flew all around the room like the scene from *Alice in Wonderland*.

'Don't torture yourself,' Sara said, moving to him, bending to kiss his cold white cheek.

'I let her down. I should have been the one to comfort her and I didn't have the nerve.'

'You did the best thing,' Sara assured him. Anxiously she saw that he was looking ill, his face totally without colour, a muscle twitching in his cheek and a reflex under his eye making the whole lid quiver.

'She just sat there. I thought she was dying. She was like someone in a desert, a wasteland. And I couldn't do a thing. I had to send for you.' It was obsessing him, his own failure, as he saw it.

She turned to make the cocoa and surreptitiously slipped one of Lucy's sleeping pills into it. 'Drink this and go to bed,' she said.

Greg looked at it with distaste. 'I don't really want it,' he told her.

She held it to his lips as though he was a child and

he grimaced and drank. She heard him stumble as he went up the stairs to the spare room which he was using. Sara had elected to sit up all night. She wanted to be awake if Lucy cried out, and at four in the morning Lucy did wake up, crying weakly until Sara hushed her back to sleep. She sat all night on the landing in the little house with a book open on her knees to which her eyes never turned.

A fortnight later she and Lucy flew off to the South of France to spend some weeks in a tiny cottage owned by a friend who had pressed it firmly on Lucy. Sara looked down at the blue sea as the plane banked in order to land. Since Rob's death she had barely thought of Nick. She had shut him up into a remote compartment of her mind and she firmly intended that in future he should stay there. It had been a reckless brush with passion, but she had escaped. She would never again allow herself to feel like that. She had learnt something about herself, anyway. She had never known herself to be capable of such a fierce sensual desire, but now she knew, and she would be very wary in the future. The blue sea and the green land came closer. Lucy stirred from her cold immobility and Sara touched her hand, wordless. Lucy gave her a brief tired smile. 'Look,' Sara said lightly, pointing through the window. 'The sun!'

CHAPTER FIVE

THE following April Sara drove into Suffolk to stay for a while at a country house in the flat salt marshes near the coast. The owner was a retired army officer who had commissioned her to paint a landscape of his house and grounds after seeing one of her paintings in the home of a friend. It was his son who had negotiated with her. Jeremy Forcell was something in the City, she was not sure exactly what, and his knowledge of art seemed to her minimal, but he had a roving eye and had been distinctly impressed with Sara. She wickedly suspected that the very generous fee she had been offered owed more to his having fancied her than to his father's desire to own one of her paintings.

It was nearly nine months now since Rob died. She and Lucy had spent a rather subdued few weeks in France and came back to London rapidly moving into a cold autumn, the drenched brown leaves whipped along the gutters by a bitter wind, the sky a permanent misty grey. The winter which followed had been grim. Lucy had got a job in a famous London store, more because she needed the company than because she needed the money, and although she would never be a lively spirited woman she had become gradually less like a ghost. Sara had worked obsessively, forcing herself to concentrate on it, and

83

she was aware that her reputation among those who knew anything about the subject, was growing slowly.

Greg had gone to France for three months to paint. He had earned a good deal in the previous year and he was in no urgent need of earning for a while, so he had taken a sabbatical in order to paint purely for his own pleasure. That, at least, was the story he preferred to have officially accepted. Sara suspected Greg was getting away from Lucy. He was finding it an intolerable burden to see her all the time, knowing she was alone in the house, fighting the temptation to let down his guard with her. Greg was tired. He needed a long rest.

Sara found the house with difficulty. It was called Ravens Halt, but it lay buried in a network of tiny winding marsh roads which seemed to lead in circles with the sound and smell of the sea coming and going as one drove.

When Sara finally approached it the afternoon sun was sliding down into the pearl white sea on the horizon and the house looked enormous framed in its spectral beech trees. As she came closer it diminished into a rather plain Georgian house which owed much of its beauty to the parkland setting in which it lay.

Colonel Forcell met her in a cluttered drawing-room, shaking her hand so vigorously that her fingers ached for minutes afterwards. He was a well-built iron-grey man with fierce blue eyes and a deep-toned voice like the note of Big Ben. 'Nice of

you to come,' he intoned, as though she were an
eagerly awaited visitor.

His crisp very short hair was almost entirely silver
and bristled as he moved his head. He insisted that
she take some tea and then led her around his house
showing her watercolours painted by members of
his family—all female, she noted. He seemed to believe that painting was an occupation only meant
for women.

'But you paint in oils,' he informed her, as though
she might not know. 'Messy stuff, oils.' A look of dismay came into his blue eyes. 'You don't paint in-
doors, do you?' He looked at his carpets and she
saw he was alarmed at the idea of gouts of sticky oil
paints left on them.

'That depends on the weather and how long you
want me to take,' she said.

'Ah,' he said, clearing his throat. 'Take as long as
you like. I enjoy company.' There was a brief mas-
culine gleam in the blue eyes as he surveyed her
very feminine outline. He must have been quite a
charmer in his youth, she thought, finding herself
ludicrously smiling under his gaze. His son had
something of the same effect. 'Yes, as long as you
like,' he added, his eye reverting to his threatened
carpets. Just so long as you don't drop oil around
here, Sara thought for him, grinning.

He was very proud of his home. It had been in
his family for a hundred and fifty years, he informed
her.

'Was it built for your family?' she asked.

He shook his head. 'No, no, older than that. No,

we bought it. The grounds are lovely.'

'So I noticed,' she said. 'Have you any particular vista you want me to paint?'

'I thought from the front with the beech trees and the stream,' he said a little uncertainly, eyeing her as though uncertain whether she would approve.

'That sounds fine,' she agreed, and he looked relieved. He gave her his approving smile again.

'Good, good. Saw your painting of Moberley's place. Liked it. Just the sort of thing I want.'

Sara nodded, having heard all this from his son. 'I think I can get the effect you want,' she promised. 'I'll stroll round the grounds tomorrow, if I may, to take my bearings.'

'Cover the ground,' he nodded. 'Good strategy.'

In her comfortable, rather old-fashioned bedroom, she laughed as she remembered his conversation. He was a sweetie, but she fancied she might get rather tired of his gruff barking if she had to listen to it too often.

Miraculously, spring had come early to the low-lying countryside. Suffolk was not the warmest county in England, but it had its own special beauty in the spring when wild flowers sprang thickly in the salt-drenched grass, pale pyramidal orchids, blue-eyed grass, flags and purple fritillary. The mornings and evenings came in shrouding, damp mists which dripped from tree to tree and left glistening drops on blades of grass. Sometimes the sun swam like a red coin through the mist and sometimes the day was sunless and cold. Sara drove around the district when it was too cold to paint

outdoors and stared with awed admiration and in-
credulity at the great medieval churches on their
lifted hills above the sea, the light striking through
their stained glass and giving an eerie beauty to
their emptiness. They had been built in the days
when this area was rich because of the quiet sheep
still cropping today on the level fields. The wool
merchants of England had wisely piled their trea-
sures in heavens, building magnificent churches
which lived long after wool had ceased to bring such
wealth to the county. Now the churches lay in the
empty fields like stranded galleons and the shivering mists crept through them night and day.

Sara had been at Ravens Halt a week and made
little progress with her picture when Jeremy Forcell
came down for the weekend. He was a very charming young man, fair and tanned, with a quick smile
and an eye which held a very male interest as he
looked at Sara.

'You don't want to work at a weekend,' he informed her on the Saturday morning. 'Put your
brushes away and play.'

'Play what?' she asked, looking at him through
her lashes, a teasing smile on her lips.

He grinned. 'This and that,' he retorted. 'There's
a boat on the stream. Have you been out in it yet?'

'It looked unsafe to me,' Sara said warily.

'Rubbish,' Jeremy retorted lightly, and dragged
her down to the wide weed-choked stream which ran
through the grounds. The boat floated, but that was
all that could be said about it. They had to bail most
of the time since it shipped water at an alarming

rate, but somehow this made them both laugh a good deal, especially when Jeremy scooped water over his own legs instead of throwing it out of the boat. They spent an enjoyable morning playing the fool in the boat and after a leisurely lunch they played the fool on the distinctly uneven tennis court which hadn't been properly mowed for a long time. The ball flew all over the place and often did not bounce because it hit a patch of moss. But they enjoyed themselves.

Jeremy played extremely badly, as Sara told him, but she suspected that that was largely because he spent so much time looking at the long smooth gleam of her legs as she chased the ball across the grass. She had brought no shorts with her, so she had borrowed a very brief white tennis skirt which belonged, Jeremy told her, to his sister Annabel, who was in London.

'She won't mind,' he assured her.

'Are you sure?'

He nodded. 'Annabel has dozens of clothes she never even wears. She's an extravagant girl. That's why she's in London—keeping a watchful eye out for a millionaire.'

Not believing his light chatter, Sara laughed. 'How sensible!'

'She'll need one,' Jeremy groaned. 'Spends money like water. I can't imagine how my father manages to support her.'

'She doesn't work?' As soon as she had asked the question Sara knew from his wry grin that it was a stupid one.

'Annabel work? My dear girl, you're joking!'

'How old is she?'

'Twenty,' Jeremy said. 'Well, that's what it says on her birth certificate and I must admit I seem to have known her around that long, but she acts more as though she were twelve.'

Sara laughed. 'Pretty, though, I imagine?'

'Now why should you imagine that?' The brightness of his eyes told her that he imagined she was inferring Annabel's looks from his and she shook her head teasingly at him.

'If she hopes to catch a millionaire she'll need to be.'

Jeremy looked amused. 'Oh, Annabel is pretty.' He glanced at her with that glint in his eyes. 'But you're a knock-out—but you know that, don't you?'

'Do I?' she asked demurely.

'I can't be the first man to tell you so.'

'I don't believe everything I hear.' Her smile faded slightly as she thought of one man who had told her she was beautiful, but then she pushed the thought away and deliberately smiled at Jeremy again.

'You can believe that,' he told her. 'Any mirror would tell you. In that tiny skirt you're incredibly sexy. I can't believe you're a painter. Are you good?'

Sara opened her eyes wide. 'You mean you don't know? I thought you'd seen some of my work.'

'Dad did,' he shrugged. 'But then his idea of art beings and ends with *The Stag at Bay*.'

Sara shook her head reprovingly. 'So wrong. Your father likes soft little watercolours. I think he would rather have something like that from me—more feminine than oils.'

Jeremy looked surprised. 'Did he say so?'

'No, I read his mind.'

'Can you read mine?' He leered dramatically at her, his eyes sweeping over her curved body in the short-sleeved white shirt and brief skirt.

'I wish I couldn't,' she retorted, moving back towards the house.

Jeremy's laughter came after her. Although he was making very obvious passes at her, he was an even-tempered man, charmingly casual, light-hearted and distinctly labelled 'Not to be taken seriously'. Sara had enjoyed her day with him, but she suspected that too much of his company would bore her. She was used to brittle repartee from Greg in certain moods, but Greg was basically an entirely serious man. The light teasing obscured his real nature, and Sara preferred it like that.

He stayed until the Monday and Sara was permanently in his company. She observed with interest his relationship with his father, surprised and impressed by it. Jeremy behaved perfectly in his father's company, treating the Colonel with the calm respect of a junior officer to a senior, a relationship which Sara saw at once exactly suited the Colonel's frame of mind. Jeremy noted her eyes on them and when they were alone on the Sunday afternoon he commented on it rather wryly.

'Don't miss much, do you?'

She opened her eyes. 'Meaning?'

'You remind me of the old saying about a child

among us taking notes. Your eyes are as sharp as needles.'

'Careful they don't prick you, then,' she retorted, looking at him with a teasing little smile.

The already familiar rakish smile drifted over his face. He lowered his tone and his face. 'Perhaps they already have.'

'You are a terrible flirt,' she returned with amused driness.

'You're not?' His brows curved upward, their fairness lost in the pale tan of his skin.

'Do you think I am?' She looked surprised and Jeremy gave her a wicked grin.

'You know damned well you are.'

That surprised her because she had always thought of herself as serious-minded. To cover her chagrin she changed the subject. 'What exactly do you do in the City?'

'Work like a slave,' he groaned, his face changing. 'Nine to five drudgery five days a week.'

'How terrible,' she mock-sympathised.

'Don't laugh,' he muttered. 'You've no idea of the amount of tedium one can suffer in the cause of earning a living.'

'No?' she asked, her eyes ironical.

He met her glance and grinned. 'I don't quite like your expression, Miss Nichols. I hope you're not implying that I'm tedious?'

She didn't answer, grinning. 'If you don't like your job, why not change it?'

His eyes had a serious look for a fleeting second. 'I didn't say I didn't like it. It can be very satisfying, but I have a boss who has some resemblance to Simon Legree. I hear his whip cracking behind me from morning to night.'

'Poor Jeremy,' she soothed. 'I hope you'll go back to London nicely rested and relaxed, anyway.'

'Oh, yes,' he agreed with his eyes on her. 'I've had a marvellous weekend. How long are you staying?'

'Until my work's finished.'

'How long will that be?'

She shrugged. 'That depends. A few more weeks. The weather hasn't been ideal, but it's getting better every day.'

'May I come down next weekend?' he asked.

She looked down. 'It's your home.'

'You know what I'm asking,' Jeremy said very softly.

She looked up. A frown crossed her face. 'I have no interest in a serious relationship, Jeremy.'

Laughter showed in his eyes. 'My God, neither have I, woman.'

She laughed back then, relaxing. 'I see.' Her tone was rueful and mocking.

'And so?' he pressed.

'And so why not?' she retorted.

He kept his word and reappeared the following weekend, surprising his father, who had not expected him to come again so soon but who glanced from him to Sara with sudden realisation before tramping off discreetly to leave them alone. She had got on very well with the Colonel during that week. One rainy afternoon she spent four hours painting a delicate little watercolour for him and saw his heavy face light up.

'My word, that's good,' he had said, confirming her suspicion that he was drawn to the delicacy of the medium. When she gave him the small picture he seemed quite touched, coughing loudly because he could not think of a thing to say, and he took her off with him to choose a place to hang it among his other family watercolours. Several times since she had found him standing in front of it, gazing at it, and she found it rather sad that in all probability he would always prefer it to the oil painting she was doing for him.

Jeremy monopolised her that weekend. They walked and talked, drove around the windy Suffolk lanes, listened to records and argued about cricket, for which Jeremy had a passion. Sara had teased him by saying it was a silly game, amused to see him flare up angrily, for once excited in his disbelief at her viewpoint.

'Doesn't your sister ever come down to see her father?' Sara asked him.

Jeremy shrugged. 'Now and then. Annabel is a town bird. The country bores her.'

'It doesn't bore you?'

His eyes had that quick gleam. 'Not when you're around.'

She pushed that aside. 'Apart from that?'

Jeremy looked pensively at the flat green fields and grey sky. 'I am rather fond of the place. No, I don't get bored although I like London. This is my home, and there's a special feeling for a place you've always known. Don't you think?'

She nodded. 'I'm sure there is, but I've always lived near London.'

'Got a flat?' he asked. 'You haven't told me much about your own family. Are there many of you?'

'Just me and Greg, my stepbrother,' she said. 'Our parents are dead. I've no other relatives.'

He frowned. 'You don't surprise me. You've got a rather self-contained face.'

'Such shrewdness,' she mocked lightly.

'My old dad has taken quite a fancy to you,' he said. 'I've never known him so taken with anyone. Usually he's something of a recluse, not a gregarious type at all.'

'He's a darling,' Sara said impulsively. 'Under that bristling manner he's really as soft as butter.'

'Hey!' Jeremy gave her a quick look. 'I don't see you in the role of stepmother, you know.'

Her lips twisted. 'What role do you see me in?'

He didn't answer, grinning wickedly at her.

'Think again,' Sara retorted reprovingly. She was not sure exactly how serious he was about his interest in her, but somehow did not imagine he had marriage in mind. Although she enjoyed the light flirtation she was having with him she did not want to get any deeper involved. Jeremy was charming as an occasional companion, but there it stopped.

When he had returned to London, however, she found the house very empty without him. His amusing banter was infectious. She missed him. She worked on her canvas at a steady pace, knowing it would soon be finished but wanting to give the Colonel good value for his money. The effect she wanted to obtain was not easy. She was hoping to persuade him that an oils could be as visually effective as the softer, more subtle watercolours he really preferred, and that involved far more concentrated attention to detail.

She was surprised when Jeremy appeared on the Friday afternoon, throwing her a coaxing grin. 'I want to take you up to town,' he told her. 'Annabel's throwing a party. Will you come?'

'I haven't got a suitable dress,' she said regretfully. In fact, she was delighted at the idea of a party. She had spent weeks now in a deep attention to work and she was in the mood to have fun.

'I could drive you to your flat to pick one up,' he suggested.

She only had her black crêpe trouser suit or her silver dress and suddenly she felt like buying something new. She rarely went to parties and her wardrobe was rather limited. Although she was earning more each year, she wasn't yet fully established and her fees were hardly astronomic. She tended to buy clothes she could wear for a long time, functional clothes, hard-wearing clothes. She looked at Jeremy and felt suddenly reckless.

'I'll buy a new one,' she said.

He caught her mood, grinning. 'That's the idea! Bonnet over the windmill?'

She lowered her lashes demurely. 'I don't know what you mean.'

He drove her to London, stopping off on the way so that she could hurriedly dive into a small but expensive little boutique in a back street of Colchester. It was five o'clock when they reached the town and Colchester was winding down to close for the night. The streets were full of people making their way home, cars bumper to bumper in the traffic jam which filled the centre of the city. Sara tried on several dresses, but it was Jeremy who insisted on the one which she finally bought; a very simple peacock blue shift in a silky material which glittered as she turned from side to side to survey it in the mirror. The simplicity of the cut more than offset the brilliance of the colour and her hair flamed above it dramatically.

When they came out of the shop, the homeward rush had become frenetic. They stopped to have tea in a teashop in the main street and then walked slowly along to admire the outside of the little theatre nearby, the white façade giving elegance to the new shopping areas more recently built beside it.

'Colchester has changed beyond recognition,' Jeremy told her. 'When I was a boy I used to come here often. Dad used to like buying books at the old bookshop down the hill here, and I used to leave him there and wander off to look at the Roman wall or the old houses. I think it's lost a lot of its charm in the last five years. All this redevelopment may be good for business, but it certainly knocks hell out of the look of the place.'

'I don't really know it,' Sara admitted.

'A lot of new houses have been built near the city. Essex is expanding fast. Natural enough, I suppose, as it's so near London.'

'Are you a conservationist?' she asked drily, smiling.

'I just hate to see things change,' Jeremy admitted with a self-deriding smile.

'Don't we all? It's inbuilt with us.'

'The human condition?' Jeremy asked, his eyes on his face.

She looked up. 'Yes.'

'You've used that phrase to me several times, but I'm not sure what you mean by it.'

'It covers a multitude of sins,' she shrugged. 'People are weird.'

'There's nowt so queer as folk?' he suggested, lips twitching.

'Absolutely nowt,' she agreed, laughing.

'I prefer that phrase,' he told her. 'I'm very down to earth.'

'So I'd noticed,' Sara said silkily.

In the car as they drove into London along the fast motorway, she asked: 'Tell me more about Annabel. What does she do all day if she doesn't have a job?'

'She has one of sorts, but not what you would call a job,' he said with a wry face. 'She helps out at a Bond Street shop for a few hours a day. When she's in the mood. There's nothing so limiting as actual working hours for Annabel. If she gets up in time, she drops in there and condescends to sell a few items, if pressed by customers.'

'Don't tell me; it's owned by a friend?'

'Admirer,' Jeremy said with no smile at all. 'I can't stand the man, but he fancies Annabel and she doesn't discourage him. If her millionaire doesn't turn up trumps she may even marry him, God help her.'

She considered his face. 'You really don't like him, do you?'

'Detest him,' Jeremy muttered. 'He's far too old for her, but she wouldn't listen if I said a word. Annabel is stubborn. She's been following this crazy dream of hers for two years and it's got her nowhere.'

'She wants to be rich?'

'That and other things,' Jeremy muttered again. He drew back his shoulders and gave her a smile. 'Can we talk about something more pleasant? How's the picture coming?'

'Nearly finished. And I'm quite pleased with it.'

'Dad seen it yet?'

'Oh, no,' she said, horrified. 'Not until I've finished it. Not on your life! It would put me off.'

They had dinner in London, taking their time, and arrived at Annabel's flat soon after nine. She lived in a district of Kensington Sara had only visited once or twice—high, gabled Victorian houses clustered together, their enormous floor space long since given over to flats and bedsitters. Annabel lived on the ground floor of one. Cars were parked like sardines around it and the sound of throbbing music met them as they arrived at the front door.

A young man opened it at Jeremy's insistent ring. Jeremy gave him a nod. 'Hallo, David.' He dragged Sara past him and forced a way past the chattering groups of people to meet his sister.

She turned from the people she was talking to, giving a groan. 'Oh, you've come, have you?'

'Charming,' said Jeremy. 'Annabel, this is Sara. She's painting a picture of the house for Dad.'

Annabel gave her a sweet, bright smile which

didn't quite reach her golden-brown eyes. 'Hi, Sara.'
The eyes swept over Sara's slender figure in the
gleaming peacock dress. Sara had somehow expected to see a version of Jeremy, but Annabel did not
look like him at all. She had a glossy sophisticated
prettiness which did not seem to reach her eyes. The
smooth dark-brown bell of hair curved round her
face, the vivid red of her mouth matched by her
long, manicured nails.

'Marvellous to see you,' she said, and didn't mean
a word of it. She glanced away from Sara to her
brother. 'Drinks in the other room,' she told him,
and turned back to her friends.

Jeremy looked at her back with unhidden anger,
but Sara took his hand and moved away.

'Rotten manners. I'm sorry,' he said, following
her.

'It doesn't matter,' Sara shrugged.

'It matters to me,' Jeremy retorted. 'I can't stand
Annabel when she's in that sort of mood. Who the
hell does she think she is?'

'Forget it. We're here for the party, not to have
your sister welcoming me with open arms.'

The party was enjoyable. Jeremy knew many of
the guests and was hailed with delight by them.
They gave Sara the same warm appreciation, which
more than made up for the snub his sister had given
her. The evening wore on with dancing and laughing, quite a bit of drinking, and some idiotic games
which Jeremy organised. They found a large old
tin tray in the kitchen and Jeremy at once insisted
that they play sleighing down the stairs. Heaped

with cushions stolen from a couch they took turns in sliding bumpily down the stairs, shrieking with laughter. God knew what the neighbours thought, Sara mused.

'Come on, darling!' Jeremy yelled when she stood aloof watching them.

Protesting, she was dragged up the stairs and seated on the tray with Jeremy behind her, his arms clasped round her waist.

It was more like a nursery party than a party for grownups, Sara decided in rueful amusement.

The tray rushed noisily down the stairs and she closed her eyes in sudden alarm at the speed of it. Jeremy whooped behind her, holding her tighter. As they reached the bottom they were flung helplessly across the hall, missing the cushions which had been laid to catch them.

Jeremy rolled, holding her close, and as they came to a stop he raised himself to look down, laughing, into her face. 'Darling, you look petrified,' he teased.

'You fool!' she gasped, all the breath knocked out of her.

He bent his fair head and kissed her lingeringly.

A shadow passed on the wall. Vaguely Sara glanced upwards and her heart turned over with a violence which made all the colour leave her face.

Nick walked past without looking at her, but she knew he must have seen her. Jeremy was lifting her to her feet, staring.

'Sara, you're as white as a ghost. I'm sorry, darling. Did it really scare you that much? Hit me if it will make you feel better.'

She pulled herself together, smiling too brightly. 'I'm fine.' Her glance moved to where Nick's lean dark body was disappearing into the next room. What on earth was he doing here?

'Game over,' Jeremy said to the others. They collected up the tray and cushions and vanished laughing into the other rooms. Jeremy looked down at Sara.

'You do look sick, you know. Did you hit your head or something?'

She snapped at him. 'I'm fine, I told you!'

Jeremy looked startled. It was the first time she had ever shown any sign of temper.

'Shall we dance?' Jeremy asked uncertainly.

She nodded, giving him a rueful look. 'I'm sorry. It knocked me for six.'

She was aware of a hidden irony even as she said it. The ride down the stairs hadn't really bothered her at all. It was seeing Nick which had made her feel as though she had been flung off the edge of the world and even as she followed Jeremy into the room where people were dancing, she was finally facing a fact which she had refused to face for a long time. She was in love with Nick Rawdon.

It was something she had never wanted to happen and something which she had imagined was all over for her. She hadn't seen him for months, yet that one brief glimpse had left her in a state of shock. Her skin felt cold, her heart was pounding, her stomach was churning. She moved in Jeremy's arms with her eyes closed because she couldn't quite see the room. It was dipping and whirling in a funny way. Jeremy took advantage of her weakness, of course. He gathered her close and crooned softly against her ear, his mouth brushing her cheek, her neck. Sara was almost unconscious of him. Behind her closed lids she was seeing Nick again and again, the averted hard face, the lithe body moving at a stride.

What had he thought? Or hadn't he even recognised her? Had he forgotten her in the past nine months?

Probably, she thought. Why should he remember her? He had made a few passes and then decided she wasn't worth the effort. There must have been a dozen others in his life since then. She hadn't followed his romantic adventures in the glossy magazines, but once Greg had looked up from glancing through one and asked if she had read some gossip item about her merchant banker and a blonde model. 'Apparently he just dropped her and she's crying all over the Sunday papers, no doubt making a fortune at the same time.'

Sara hadn't even glanced at the picture he held out to her. Her face had been blank. 'Lucky escape for her,' she had merely commented with a brittle smile, and Greg had dropped the subject.

Sara had no illusions about how Nick would have spent the past nine months. He had never pretended to be a plaster saint and his technique with women wouldn't have been learnt at Sunday school. She didn't like it—but then she didn't intend to make it her business to like or dislike anything Nick Rawdon did.

'Angel, you are so sexy,' Jeremy whispered, and she opened her eyes carefully to smile at him.

Over his shoulder she met a pair of hard blue eyes and felt that violent shock again.

She moved her own eyes away back to Jeremy and smiled up into his eyes, a brilliant smile to which Jeremy responded like a seal flung a piece of fish.

He kissed her as they danced and she made no attempt to move away. Her pulses were racing so wildly that she felt she might be sick and as Jeremy moved back he looked astonished. 'Darling, you're blushing,' he commented, and she knew from the heat burning in her face that he was right, but it had nothing to do with him. She didn't look towards Nick. He was dancing beside them with Annabel in his arms. Sara had seen that at a glance, but she wouldn't look his way again.

Jeremy's eyes were excited. 'Am I getting somewhere at last?' he asked her very softly, and she sighed, realising that he was misunderstanding her obvious reactions.

'Don't take me seriously, Jeremy,' she warned in a low tone.

Jeremy's rakish smile flashed out. 'If you say so,' he returned. 'But you are giving me quite a come-on, you know.'

She did know and she felt furious with herself. She had been using him to disguise from Nick her reaction to him and it was a disgusting thing to do. She looked at Jeremy wryly.

'It must be the drink.'

'Ah,' he said. 'One damned gin after another?'

She giggled at the quote and Jeremy laughed back at her. He wasn't taking her seriously and that was a relief. She liked Jeremy, but he wasn't for her. Out of the corner of her eye she saw Nick again, his black head bent down towards Annabel, whose glossy little head was nestling on his broad shoulder. Damn her, Sara thought, and winced at the sheer agony of the jealousy which was stabbing inside her.

Jeremy suddenly also caught sight of Nick and his face altered. He obviously met Nick's eye because he gave him a curiously polite smile. 'Oh, hallo, sir,' he said, and Sara's eyes opened wide at the 'sir'.

Nick didn't answer. He merely nodded curtly and Sara knew he wasn't looking at her, he was keeping his eyes on Jeremy's face before he turned away.

As they moved away Jeremy whispered, 'My boss.'

Sara stiffened. 'Boss?' She was shaken by the news.

'Mr Nicholas Rawdon,' Jeremy expanded in derisory tones. 'I work at Rawdons. Didn't I tell you? It's an old merchant bank and he's the boss, the Great Panjandrum himself.'

Sara's throat felt dry. 'Democratic of him to come to your sister's party, then.'

Jeremy laughed. 'Ah, well, that's another story. He's Annabel's millionaire, her walking dream. I told you she had a terrible crush on a millionaire, didn't I? Nick's the chap.'

Sara swallowed with difficulty. 'I thought you were just talking generally. I didn't realise she actually had a special millionaire in view.'

'Not just in view,' Jeremy shrugged. 'Her campaign to get him has been going for months, but it begins to look as if she's getting somewhere. Lately he's been a lot more responsive, according to Annabel.'

Sara smiled. 'Lucky Annabel!'

That smile cost her more than anything had ever done in her life before. She was acting so hard she barely knew what she was doing. The pain was unbelievable. She thought it would never stop. It was like the stabbing of a thousand tiny knives and she wondered how it was humanly possible to smile and talk while such anguish consumed one.

As she danced in Jeremy's arms she wished fiercely for Greg. He was the only human being who could understand how she felt. Was this how he had felt whenever he thought about Lucy? God help him if it was, Sara told herself.

A few moments later she and Jeremy were beside Annabel and Nick again. Sara looked blankly past Nick, her face coolly controlled, yet seeing with a rending jealousy the way his lithe body moved against Annabel's, the strong hand on the girl's waist, his face against Annabel's cheek.

She forced herself to see them, to look and accept it. She was not going to be cowardly about this, she was going to face it. As she moved her eyes coolly over them Nick's eyes briefly glanced over at her and before she could look away their eyes had met. The blue eyes were fixed and cold. They looked right through her before they moved away. Sara laughed at that moment because Jeremy was whispering something in her ear and was waiting for her to laugh in reponse. Her laughter was bright and appreciative and Jeremy was satisfied. Nick glanced at her again and his brows were dark over the blue eyes. There was anger in his face now and suddenly she realised he thought she was laughing at him.

She had laughed at him before and he had looked at her like this, his eyes savage.

Why has this happened to me? she thought. I wish to God I'd never set eyes on him.

CHAPTER SIX

IT was half an hour later that Sara found herself facing Nick again. She and Jeremy were in a large, noisy group laughing at one side of the room. Sara had deliberately not been allowing her eyes to wander because she did not want to see Nick again. She hoped he would leave before they were ever brought in contact. Suddenly the young men in the group glanced past her and their faces changed, sobered. Jeremy looked suddenly alert, like a boy scout seeing an old lady across the road.

'Nice of you to turn up, sir,' he said, all the rakish charm going out of his face.

Sara felt a frisson of nervous alarm run down her spine. Although he didn't move she knew he was standing just behind her and when he spoke the deep cold voice was like a knife in her back.

'Enjoying yourselves, are you?'

Somehow he made that sound like an accusation. Jeremy looked at his hands and said smartly, 'You haven't got a drink, sir. Can I get you something?'

'Thank you. Whisky and soda.'

The group dissolved like magic, murmuring politely. Sara couldn't believe it. She felt panic-stricken, wondering how to walk away without betraying her dismay.

Jeremy had ducked off to get the drink. Nick didn't move, but she could feel his eyes on her, his body just behind her, hear the sound of his quiet breathing.

'How long have you known Forcell?'

She turned then, slowly, bracing herself for the impact of that hard face and their eyes met.

'A few weeks.' She made no effort to smile; it was beyond her.

His mouth twisted. 'Halliday off painting again, is he?'

Her colour rose. 'He's in France,' she said with a snap.

Nick arched the black brows. 'How lucky for Forcell. He doesn't know about Halliday, I suppose?'

She met his eyes levelly, not answering.

'Someone ought to warn him that he's wasting his time,' Nick said maliciously.

'Why don't you?' Anger made her smile mocking and the blue eyes narrowed sharply, suddenly filled with ice.

He ran his gaze down the slender body from the fine-boned shoulders past her rounded breasts to the long, slim legs. 'Or is he doing very nicely while Halliday's out of the picture? I seem to recall you've no objection to a brief romance.'

Her skin was burning but her eyes were filled with anger. She still didn't answer, although he paused to wait for a reply. While they stood there Jeremy reappeared with a glass of whisky which he handed to Nick. He looked at Sara and said, 'You haven't met, have you? Sara, this is my boss, Mr Rawdon. Sir, this is Sara Nichols, an artist, she's painting Ravens Halt for my father.'

To Sara's surprise, Nick extended his hand, as though they had never met. 'How do you do, Miss Nichols?'

She dumbly found herself letting him take her hand and suddenly remembered their first meeting, the way he had held her hand until she was forced to look at him.

This time the touch of his fingers made her pulses leap in stupid excitement and she couldn't quite meet his eyes in case he saw what was happening to her.

He released her hand and drank some of his whisky. 'Good party, isn't it?' Jeremy said brightly.

Nick drank some more whisky and put his glass down. 'Very,' he said curtly. He looked at Sara. 'Will you dance, Miss Nichols?'

No! her mind shrieked, knowing that being in his arms was going to be an ordeal she couldn't face, but she heard herself saying quietly, 'Thank you,' and then she was being guided into the shuffling throng of other guests and Jeremy was staring after them with a discontented expression.

Nick held her lightly, moving with a brief space between them, his strong face averted from her.

Her mouth was dry and she was conscious of an intolerable excitement. Once he looked down and she found herself looking at him in a helpless awareness which she couldn't break. The blue eyes rested on her with unreadable fixity, the harsh lines of his face unmoving. She felt his hand stirring on her back, the fingers splaying against her silky dress, the warmth of them reaching her skin.

The music stopped and she broke away with barely a smile, walking back to Jeremy as if she had the devil at her heels. Nick didn't follow her. She smiled at Jeremy feverishly and said she really thought they should be going. They had a long drive in front of them back to Ravens Halt, she reminded him.

He took her hand, eyeing her oddly, and went off in search of Annabel. It didn't surprise Sara to find Nick with her. Jeremy lightly informed his sister that they were going. 'We've got the drive back home to face,' he grimaced.

Nick frowned. 'You aren't driving, Jeremy? You're in no condition to drive a car. Even if you manage to drive at all, the police may well stop you. You'll have to get a taxi.'

Jeremy made a face. 'All the way to Suffolk? I don't think so, sir. Don't worry, I'm not drunk.'

'You've been drinking,' Nick retorted sharply. He threw Sara a brief cold look. 'It isn't sensible.'

She was angry and jealous and reckless. 'We'll be

perfectly all right,' she said in a sharp voice.

Annabel wound her small hand through Nick's arm. 'Darling, Jeremy knows what he's doing.'

'Like hell,' said Nick, and his tone made them all stare at him. He closed the hard mouth in a straight angry line. 'I'll drive you,' he said. 'I've barely touched anything. A couple of glasses of whisky won't have affected my responses.'

Jeremy looked both amazed and horrified. 'Oh, no, really, sir,' he mumbled.

Annabel was furious. 'You can't make that drive at this hour,' she protested. 'It will take you all night to get there and back again!'

Nick had an obstinate set to his chin. 'Forcell can give me a bed for the night,' he said.

'Oh, of course,' Jeremy said unhappily, staring at his sister with an obvious shrug of resignation.

Annabel's little face smouldered with temper. She said suddenly, 'I know, why don't you and Sara stay here tonight, Jeremy? That's the answer.'

Sara turned without answering and walked to the door. She was not staying at Annabel's flat for the night. Nick strode after her and caught her arm. 'Where are you going?'

'To my own home,' she said coldly. 'I'll get a taxi. I'll see Jeremy in the morning.'

Annabel and Jeremy had rushed after Nick and Annabel looked happier now, clapping her hands. 'Sure? Well then, that's settled, isn't it?'

'I'll drive you,' said Nick without even looking at her.

'No, thank you,' Sara retorted. 'I'll get a taxi.'

Nick's hand clamped over her arm and she was hustled to the door before she could protest. She caught a glimpse of Annabel, red and gasping, and Jeremy staring in bolt-eyed surprise, then she was out of the house and Nick was pushing her like a recalcitrant child down the garden path and into his car.

'Get your hands off me!' she muttered, struggling as he opened his car.

He didn't answer, his face set. Half lifting, half pushing, he got her into the car and slammed the door on her furious face. She turned to open it, but he was beside her in the driver's seat, reaching across to bang the door shut again. 'Do up your seat belt,' he commanded.

She sank back with fury into the seat and fiddled for the belt. Nick did not move to help, watching her with a stiff, cold expression. As soon as her belt was fastened he started the ignition. The car shot away with a roar.

Nick drove without speaking or even looking at her. Sara stared out of the window at the houses dimly passing. When he finally pulled up outside her home, she turned to open the door, and he moved then, dragging her round to face him, his hands on her shoulders.

'Oh, no! Not yet, you little bitch!'

His voice was unrecognisable, a harsh, hoarse whisper, and she looked at him in startled shock, trying to pull away as she understood his intention. His hands moved up to trap her head, holding it immovable, and then his mouth crushed down hungrily, parting her lips.

Desire fountained crazily inside her. She heard the intake of his breath as their mouths explored each other even more deeply, then they both moved, their bodies meeting, clinging, in a feverish impact which erased everything else from her mind. Sara was dissolving into him, her hands clasping his neck. The passion they had exchanged the night she went to his penthouse seemed suddenly a milk-and-water thing compared to the almost desperate urgency between them now.

The months since they last met had not weakened Nick's attraction for her. It had strengthened it. In the dark forcing-house of her emotions this love had been growing without her knowledge, and now it was thrusting upwards to the light, eager to flower, and she was helpless to fight the hot necessity of it.

His hands were moving urgently down her body, warm on the cool skin, sliding sensuously over the silky material which clung so closely to her body.

She arched towards him in response to those coaxing hands, her eyes shut tight, her breathing deafening her. She barely knew what she was doing, trembling and helpless in the grip of her wild response to him.

Nick wasn't giving her time to think, either, his caresses becoming more intimate with every moment. His mouth wasn't moving from hers, covering it, holding it, and his hands cupped her breasts as he leaned over her, her body trapped by his against the seat.

She suddenly felt she was suffocating under the hard invasion of his lips and as if Nick sensed it he drew back slightly, breathing hard.

Eyes closed, she lay quivering, arms still round his neck, and he pushed his hot face into her neck, his lips moving on her skin.

The coldness, the anger, had gone out of his voice when he spoke again and he sounded as dazed as she felt. 'I want you so much, darling. Let me come in, let me stay with you tonight,' he whispered, kissing her throat. 'For God's sake, let me stay with you.' He felt her trembling and lifted his head to look at her, his eyes pleading. 'Sara, let me love you.'

There was nothing she wanted more and she would have said yes with unthinking eagerness, but Lucy was there. She had had to sell her house after Rob's death and she had moved in with Sara while Greg was away in France and Lucy's new flat was being redecorated.

'I can't,' she almost sobbed, and Nick stiffened.

He drew back and looked at her through the darkness, his face cruel. 'Afraid Halliday will find out?'

'There's someone there,' she said miserably, and Nick swore so viciously that she jumped, incredulous.

'Damn you to hell!' he said hoarsely. 'Get out of my car.'

Trembling, white-faced, Sara got out and Nick shot away with a screech of tyres, leaving her standing on the pavement in total shock.

She stumbled into the house and as she closed the door she fainted. The slump of her body woke Lucy. She came running in alarm from her bedroom in Sara's half of the house and switched on the light, half expecting to see a burglar, no doubt. Sara came to a moment later to find Lucy kneeling beside her, exclaiming in shocked anxiety.

'I'm all right,' she mumbled, her lips bruised and hot.

'What's wrong?' Lucy asked with a worried look. 'You're white!'

Sara laughed wildly. 'I'm fine, just fine.'

'You don't look fine,' Lucy observed, frowning.

Sara got shakily to her feet and Lucy put an arm round her, supporting her.

'What are you doing here? I thought you were still in Suffolk. Why have you arrived back at this hour?'

Sara was still unstrung, still half out of her mind. Without thinking she said wildly, 'I wish to God Greg was here!'

Lucy looked at her in sharp inspection. 'What's wrong, Sara? Can't I help?'

Sara began to pull herself together. 'No, no, forget it. Lucy, I could be very grateful for a cup of strong tea.'

'I'll get you one,' Lucy said at once, delighted to be of some use. 'First, let's get you into bed, shall we?'

'I can manage,' said Sara, forcing a smile. 'Really, I'm fine.'

'People don't faint for nothing,' Lucy said, then

gave her a strange intent look. 'Go ahead, then, get into bed while I make some tea.'

Sara made her way into her own bedroom and undressed. Lucy came along with the tea a few minutes later and looked at her in assessment.

'Thank you. I'm dying for this,' Sara said, sipping the tea.

'Anything else you want?' Lucy asked her.

Sara shook her head. 'I'm sorry I disturbed you. You mustn't worry about me. I shall be all right. I've had a bit of a shock, that's all.' Her lips twisted. 'The past suddenly caught up with me with a vengeance!'

Lucy went out and Sara finished her tea and settled down to sleep. She was not surprised that it evaded her. She lay in the darkness, twisting uneasily, remembering Nick's passion. He had wanted her and frustration had made him furious. He must think she had been playing with him. The glittering flash of his eyes as he told her to get out of his car had been almost manic. Would be go back to the party? Back to Annabel, who was so eager for his attention? Annabel, though, was holding out for marriage, no doubt, and Sara knew enough about Nick by now to know that he was by no means eager to enter matrimony. He enjoyed his freedom. He had the money to buy whatever he wanted and he would have a varied love life, she imagined. Marriage would limit his freedom.

Damn him, I hope Annabel does pull it off, she thought. I'd like to think of him caged and having his wings clipped!

She remembered the smooth sophistication he had

worn when they first met and contrasted it with the
entirely primitive rage which had glared out of his
eyes as he swore at her before throwing her out of
his car. He was a selfish swine. They hadn't set eyes
on each other for nine months, yet the moment he
had her alone he was trying to persuade her into
bed and becoming violent when she had to turn
him down. He hadn't even pretended to care two-
pence for her. He had spoken to her, looked at her,
with harsh contempt mixed with the desire his body
had given away as he held her.

She slept at last, worn out, and was pale and heavy-
eyed in the morning when Lucy brought her a
cup of tea. Jeremy rang at eleven, sounding as
though he had been put through a wringer. 'What
time shall I pick you up? I've just got up, I'm
afraid.'

'Good party after I'd gone?' she asked brightly.

He groaned. 'Unfortunately, yes. My head is
throbbing.'

Your head! Sara thought. Mine is like a tin can
full of marbles. It was rattling painfully every time
she moved her neck.

They agreed that she should be picked up after
lunch. Jeremy yawned. 'See you, angel.'

She had not asked if Nick had come back to the
party. She didn't want to know. Let him. She didn't
care.

Lucy looked dismayed when Sara said she was
driving back to Suffolk at once. 'But I didn't realise
you meant to go back! I thought you'd left there
for good.'

'No, I haven't finished my picture yet. I came up to London for a party last night, but now I'm going back to do the last work. I should only be there for a few more days.'

Lucy chewed her lower lip, her face distracted. 'Oh, dear!'

Sara looked at her in surprise. 'What's wrong, Lucy? I'm fine now, I promise you.'

Lucy gave her a quick, nervous look, her face becoming very flushed. 'I rang Greg.'

'What?' Sara stared at her. 'Why on earth did you do that?' Then she realised. 'Because I fainted? Oh, Lucy, what did you say to him? You shouldn't have worried him.'

Lucy wasn't looking at her. The dark hair hung limply around her face and her eyes were restless.

'I told him I thought he should come back at once, that you needed him ... well, you said so. You said you wished he was here.'

Sara couldn't remember having said it. She was merely horrified to hear that Greg had been distressed like this over nothing. 'Why on earth did you do it? Whatever I said, I wouldn't want Greg worried.'

'He ought to be here,' Lucy said stubbornly. 'Why should you go through this on your own?'

'Through what?' Sara felt herself blushing deeply. When she was still barely conscious last night had she said something about Nick? Made some unguarded remark to give Lucy a clue to what had made her faint?

Lucy looked at her pink face and her eyes were

angry. 'Don't look like that. I'm not passing any judgment, Sara. Greg loves you, and now he knows you're carrying his child ...'

'*What?*' Sara's voice soared, incredulous, stricken.

Lucy met her eyes and a slow uncertainty came into her face. 'You are, aren't you?'

'My God!' Sara moaned. 'My God, what have you said to Greg?'

Lucy put her hands to her face. 'You mean you aren't?'

They stared at each other in a silence which went on for ages.

'How could you, Lucy?' Sara asked in high fury. 'How could you?'

'You fainted and you said it was the past catching up with you and you wished Greg were here,' Lucy gabbled, still clasping her white face with both hands. 'And I said to Greg.' She stopped dead. Swallowed. 'I took it that you and Greg ...'

'I think that's obvious,' Sara said drily. What in heaven's name had Greg thought? Her eyes focused sharply on Lucy's horrified face. How on earth could Lucy be so blind? It seemed Nick wasn't the only one to misread the situation. Perhaps others, too, had thought that she and Greg were lovers, had turned a blind eye to it, not caring. Had she been living in a fool's paradise in believing that nobody but Nick suspected such things?

'Greg is my stepbrother, Lucy,' Sara said drily. 'Nothing more, nothing less. He never has been my lover and I wouldn't want him to be.' Her mouth contracted. 'He wouldn't want to be, either. We've never felt anything for each other but affection.'

'How was I to know?' Lucy asked fiercely. 'You always seemed so happy together. I just took it for granted.'

Sara moved to the telephone. 'I must ring Greg.'

'He won't be there,' Lucy said huskily. 'He's on his way home now.'

Sara whirled and Lucy flinched away from her, her eyes very wide. 'I'm sorry,' she whispered, her lips trembling. She covered her face with her hands. 'Oh, what must he be thinking? I said such things to him!'

'What did you say?' Sara was pale now, realising suddenly what it must have done to Greg to have Lucy speak to him like that, have her accusing him of making Sara pregnant. Poor Greg, she thought in horror. He must have been shattered!

Lucy shook her head weakly, unable to reply. What was the point of being angry with her? The small, pale face was so vulnerable, so stricken, and Sara was accustomed to being gentle with Lucy. She couldn't stay angry with her for long. Lucy had borne enough for one lifetime.

'Oh, well,' she said, trying to sound calm. 'Never mind, Greg will forgive you. You meant well—I realise that. It was all a ghastly mistake. What we need now is a cup of coffee, Lucy, a strong cup of coffee.'

Lucy was pathetically eager to make it. She had always used domestic tasks to ease her grief and anxiety. She expressed herself in action. She did things for people because she found it hard to say what she felt.

While Lucy made the coffee, Sara rang Jeremy to explain that she wouldn't be going back to Suffolk that day. 'My brother is coming home and I have to be here,' she explained, and Jeremy said he would come and pick her up the following morning in that case. 'I'll enjoy the drive,' he yawned. 'I'm glad not to have to make it today. I'm worn out.'

She agreed and rang off. Lucy had made the coffee and nervously hovered while she drank it, asking, 'Do you think Greg will be very cross?'

Sara shook her head, looking at her with a smile. 'Not with you, Lucy.' Never with you, she thought, but you apparently don't know that, my poor myopic Lucy.

What did Greg see in her to make him so faithful, so helpless to alter his feelings? Lucy was not beautiful nor was she brilliant. She was small and slight and delicate with black hair which could look limp and lifeless when she wasn't well and eyes which had faint shadows under them. Yet Greg hungered for a touch of her hand, watched her when she was unaware of him, spent hours endlessly drawing her.

'I must get some fresh air,' Sara said. 'My head aches. Can I do some shopping for you, Lucy?'

'Oh, thank you,' Lucy said eagerly. 'I must tidy up before Greg arrives.'

Sara smiled and went out, amused to see Lucy's invariable reaction once more. Now Lucy would work doggedly to make the flat beautiful for Greg's arrival in the hope of lessening his annoyance over her mistake.

It never occurred to Sara to warn Lucy not to go into Greg's flat. She herself had never ventured there without invitation, respecting Greg's privacy and knowing his secrecy about his private world.

She did the shopping Lucy had asked her to do and walked slowly around the nearby park, breathing in the cool spring air and watching a dog running in excited circles on the grass.

When she came back she saw a taxi at the gate and Greg turned from it to give her a quick, searching look. Sara slid her hand through his arm and leaned on him, sighing. 'Panic over, darling. Lucy jumped to mad conclusions just because I fainted. I am not in the family way, nor do I expect to be.'

Greg swore. 'Hell's bells,' he muttered through his teeth. 'I flew back like a madman. Lucy made it sound urgent. I thought you were at death's door. I thought Rawdon had got what he wanted after all and you were carrying the can.'

She flushed hotly. 'Well, forget it. I'm sorry, Greg. I didn't know what Lucy was up to. Don't be angry with her. She's quite petrified now she knows what she's done.'

Greg's face changed. 'Is she? Poor silly darling!' He walked away up the path and opened the door, halting suddenly. Sara came in behind him and collided with him. Lucy was walking down the stairs with her hands full of sheaves of paper, her face white.

Greg turned to stone. Sara looked at the papers Lucy was holding and felt her stomach clench in horror. Lucy had found the sketches Greg had done of her. She was staring at Greg with enormous, incredulous eyes.

Sara closed the door, trying to think. What on earth could anyone say? Lucy slowly held the sketches out to Greg, who didn't move. He was looking at the wall, his face blank.

One of the sketches floated away across the hall. Sara saw words scribbled across the foot of it, saw Lucy in a gesture of pensive grief, her face drawn with careful observation, and saw too the words written under it, knew that Lucy must have read them too, and that there could no longer be any doubt that Lucy knew how Greg felt.

She hurriedly turned and went into her own flat, leaving them alone.

My love, my love, Greg had written, and Sara was flushing deeply, remembering the words. She felt shocked at having read them. She shouldn't have done it: it was like spying. Greg would hate this. He would be sick and angry and self-hating when he realised that Lucy had seen his sketches, read his passionate words of love.

They had to deal with this themselves. Greg wouldn't thank her for having seen any of it. He would resent it.

She heard nothing from the hall, but she carefully withdrew into her own bedroom with the door shut just in case she might hear something. She put on her transistor and kept busy tidying her chest

of drawers, playing music loudly to drown any
sounds from outside. Oh, Greg, she thought, my
poor Greg. What must he be going through? Even
her own grief over Nick was paling into insignifi-
cance. In all probability, Greg had just lost Lucy
for good. The revelation of how he felt would put
an end to any chance for the future because Greg,
once exposed, was going to run and keep running.
He wasn't going to be able to go on seeing Lucy,
knowing that she knew how he felt and couldn't
respond. What was going to happen now?

She was so busy that she didn't realise anyone
was in the room until she felt Lucy behind her, and
looked quickly, searchingly at her.

Lucy sat down on her bed and twined her fingers
in her lap. 'Why didn't you tell me?'

'You're joking!'

Lucy looked up, her face flushed. 'Did you know?'

Sara nodded, watching her. What had happened
between her and Greg out there in the hall? Had
Greg gone off to lick his wounds in privacy upstairs?
What had all this done to him?

'I'm so staggered,' Lucy said suddenly. 'I had no
idea—not a suspicion. When I saw those sketches
I was curious, of course, and flattered, because
they're so good. I stood there looking through them
and it slowly dawned on me. I couldn't take it in at
first, and then I heard you coming in and I came
down and Greg looked at me, and I was sure.'

'I don't think we should be talking about it,'
Sara said. Greg would hate it if he knew Lucy was
discussing it with her. He would be outraged.

'I've got to talk to someone!' Lucy sounded distraught, her eyes wide and still oddly shocked. 'I've
thought for so long that it was you and Greg. Every-
body did. I wondered why you never married him.
The two of you seemed so devoted and there was
never any talk of anybody else for either of you,
although, heaven knows, plenty of women have
chased Greg over the last few years—he's so attractive. It wasn't surprising. But he never even looked
at anybody else and I thought it was because of you.'

Sara saw that she had no option but to let Lucy
talk it out. She sat down beside her and took Lucy's
nervously twisting fingers into her hands. 'What did
you say to Greg just now?'

'What could I say? I barely said a word.'

Sara flinched. Greg, my poor Greg, she thought.

'To think I brought him back because I thought
you were having his baby! And I said such cruel
things to him. I suppose I should have realised then
that it mattered to me what Greg did. I was angry
with him, shocked, and I let him see it.'

Sara looked at her quickly. In soft tentative tones
she asked: 'It mattered to you, then?'

'More than I realised,' Lucy said, her pale, delicate face wry. She hesitated. 'I didn't know what
to say to him just now. It's too soon. Far too soon.'
She got up hurriedly. 'I think I'll see to the dinner.'

Sara stared after her retreating back. Lucy was
doing what she always did in times of distress,
running off to her kitchen, plunging into the activ-
ity she knew best and felt safest with, alarmed and
wary, like a shy animal.

Sara dared not go to Greg to comfort him; he

wouldn't thank her for it. She sat and waited and an hour later Greg tapped on her door and came into the room. The stared at each other in silence. His face was normal, cool, but there were faint blue shadows under his eyes and Sara saw a hint of iron restraint about his sensitive mouth.

'I'm going back to France,' Greg said at last.

Sara nodded, not answering, watching him without showing any sign of reaction.

'While I'm away, get her out of here,' he said evenly. 'I couldn't live under the same roof with her.'

Sara felt herself wince at the clipped way that that was said. Greg was torn to pieces under that quiet exterior.

She took a risk because at that moment she would have taken any risk to see Greg's carefully controlled face lighten even a little.

'She was jealous when she thought I was carrying your baby,' she said, and Greg stiffened.

His eyes stayed on the floor, then rose and Sara met them directly, her face expressionless.

He didn't say anything for a long moment, then he said huskily, 'She seemed very angry when she talked to me on the phone. She sounded furious.'

'She was.' Sara bit her lower lip. 'She said it was too soon, she needs time to think.'

'She didn't say that to me,' Greg muttered. 'She didn't say a word, she just stood there, holding those damned sketches. I've burnt them,' he added viciously. 'Watched them turn to ashes. I wish I'd done it years ago.'

'Oh, Greg!' She was horrified, remembering the

beauty of them. 'Oh, how could you?'

He gave a hard laugh. 'So easily.' He moved away to the window and stared out. 'With all this, I'd forgotten what brought me back. What made you faint, Sara? Have you been ill?'

'It was nothing,' she said. 'I'd been to a party and maybe I'd had too much to drink.'

Greg swung and looked at her. 'You don't lie very well,' he said, but then he smiled. 'I won't press you for answers you don't want to give. If you do need me, you know where I am, and I'll always come if you want me.'

'I know that,' she said, and said a good deal more with her smile. Greg nodded and went out, leaving her sitting on her bed with a blank pale face. She had often wondered how Greg could go on year after year loving Lucy so hopelessly and never seeming able to break free, and now she knew because she loved Nick the same way. There was a difference, of course. She could have Nick if she was ready to accept the sort of affair he wanted, but she had no intention of doing that. While she was away from him she thought calmly and sanely about it all. It was only when she was with him, when the lure of his smile was having its effect on her, that she lost all touch with common sense. All she had to do was stay out of his company and above all out of his arms.

CHAPTER SEVEN

JEREMY drove her back to Suffolk next day, spent a few hours at the house, and left again for London. He was rather subdued, making her suspect that the party had been a hectic one after she left. Jeremy had the look of someone still recovering slowly from an appalling hangover.

She finished her painting on the following Wednesday. The Colonel clumped in front of it at her invitation and showed considerable surprise. 'Very good,' he said roughly. 'Very good indeed.'

Sara was pleased. She had tried to use the subtle colours, the soft pale washes which gave a romantic light to the Suffolk landscape and which might create the same effect as the watercolours he loved. When it was framed and hung it would not look out of place among his other paintings.

She said goodbye to the Colonel with a real sense of regret. They had got on very well together once she could discount his curt little barks of conversation and see the shy man beneath.

'Expect you'll be seeing Jeremy again,' he muttered, his eyes sly. 'Hope so. Glad you two get on.'

Sara hoped he wasn't matchmaking. She had no real interest in his son except that Jeremy was good company when he was in a lighthearted mood, but she didn't tell the Colonel that.

She had no further commissions for landscapes, but a publisher friend of Greg's rang her to ask if she was interested in doing six small plates for a book they were bringing out. Sara never refused work if she could help it, so she accepted and was sent the manuscript to read. Some of the drawings would need to contain birds which she would not find in her own garden, so she strolled along a few days later to London Zoo to find them in the great aviary.

The spring sunshine was quite hot out of the wind. She sprawled on the grass eating an orange in between drawings, watching a flamingo in the lake scooping delicately into a clump of dark reeds. The incredibly fine legs stalked away with the grace of a duchess at a garden party, the pale pink plumage ruffling slightly.

Sara heard voices coming along the path, recognised one suddenly, her heart leaping into her mouth.

She couldn't help looking. She tried to stop her eyes from moving in that direction, but she was helpless to control them.

Nick was shepherding a trio of small boys in short trousers and crisp blue shirts who were running ahead, laughing. There was a woman with them, her smooth dark hair beautifully coiffured around her bland face. She was talking now, her hand on Nick's arm, and Sara recognised her. It was his sister Judith, and from the tone of her voice she was lecturing Nick about something, although Sara was too shaken by the sight of him to hear a word she said.

Nick was listening with an irritable face, his brows black across those beautiful blue eyes.

His eyes wandered, stopped dead as he caught sight of Sara. His face changed and his body stiffened, he stopped walking and just stared at her. His sister's mouth rounded in the middle of a sentence, she gazed at Nick blankly, seeing his expression, then her head turned and Sara hurriedly looked down at her hands, plucking grass nervously, aware that her face was flaming.

She heard Nick walking over towards her and became aware that his sister had gone on ahead, her feet moving crisply. Sara heard her calling the little boys, scolding them for running ahead.

Nick's black shoes were within her angle of vision, but she didn't look up. He stood above her without speaking, but she was aware of his eyes riveted on her.

The silence seemed to elongate. She was too nervous to speak, her throat dry. His anger the last time they met had been so violent that she was frightened to look at him. She had the odd feeling that Nick didn't know what to say, either, yet he didn't go away, just stood there, looking down at her.

Suddenly he sat down on the grass beside her and at that she did look up, stealing a glance at him.

He picked a blade of grass, twirled it in his hand. 'I'm escorting my sister and her brats. What are you doing here?'

'Working.'

The monosyllable took all her nerve. It came out dry and flat.

Nick leaned over and picked up her sketchpad, flicking over the pages.

'Very good,' he said, and Sara took the pad away from him, closing it with a snap. She did not want him sitting there exchanging trite remarks with her.

'When I've put my sister and the boys into a taxi, will you have lunch with me?'

She shook her head, the vivid strands fluttering in the wind. Nick drew a long breath.

'Do I have to beg?'

She looked up then, her face almost shocked, and met his restless eyes. 'I've got to talk to you,' he said huskily.

'We've got nothing to talk about.'

'I have,' he said through his teeth.

'What?'

'The mess you're making of your life,' he said with a rasp which held a mixture of emotions, rage and bitterness and a sort of pleading.

Sara looked away again, turning her head aside. Nick leaned forward again, speaking quickly, 'Who did you have in your flat that night? Some other artist? Someone Halliday doesn't know about? Can't you sleep alone?'

She clamped her lips together, refusing to answer.

'Don't you know what you're doing to yourself? Someone has to make you see it. If you go on like this, you'll destroy yourself.' His voice was low and harsh, filled with contempt, and it hurt her. 'How many others have there been? Do you even remember?' His hand came down on her wrist, gripped so hard she felt it biting into her flesh and gasped at the pain. 'Can you even remember their faces, let alone their names?'

Her anger and hurt drove her to reckless reaction. She slapped him across the face so hard that her hand stung, and Nick jerked back, a hoarse sound coming from him. His eyes glittered at her, so angry that she thought for a moment he was going to hit her back.

The sound of running footsteps woke them both out of the appalled silence between them and Nick sprang to his feet as one of his nephews raced up to them. Sara sat, flushed and trembling, watching as Nick walked away with the child clasping his hand. Her eyes moved ahead and saw his sister standing at the end of the path, her face betraying shock and surprise.

She had seen that slap, Sara thought. She had seen Nick's almost manic reaction, the checked movement of his hand as he lifted it to hit her back. What on earth must she be thinking?

Hurriedly Sara gathered together her things and raced to the exit of the zoo, afraid that Nick would come back, urgent to get out of the place before she saw him again. She caught a taxi outside and went home to a silent flat. Lucy had moved into her own place a few days ago and Greg was still in France. Sara had the place to herself for the moment, and she was glad of the privacy. She spent a long time that evening crying like a fool, crouched on her bed. Nick's contempt had bitten into her, enraged her. Hypocrite, she thought. He's tried often enough to persuade me into bed, yet he talks in that high-minded way about what he suspects I do with others! Who does he think he is? She put her hands over her hot eyes. Why on earth hadn't she tried again to make him believe that there were no others? That his view of her was wildly wrong? When she decided to let him go on believing she was Greg's lover it hadn't meant much to her. She had not then realised she was in love with him. Now she wished to heaven she had insisted that Nick listen, believe her. His scathing view of her was painful and degrading.

She sat up later, drinking black coffee, and knew she had to make a last effort to make him believe her.

He had once invited her to see his bank. It would make a neutral territory on which they might meet without the flare-up of sexual attraction which had bedevilled every meeting they ever had. On his own ground she might get him to listen soberly, believe her. She recognised what he might think, the conclusions he might draw about her desire to clear herself with him, but she could not go on like this, knowing how he despised her.

When she drove into London the mild afternoon sunshine glittered on car metal and office windows in the crowded city streets. She had not rung to make an appointment with Nick. She was going to take a chance that he would be there and further that he would see her. It was a gamble, a game of Russian roulette she was playing with her life. If Nick wasn't there she would take it that she was not meant to tell him the truth.

She looked up at the minaret-like shadow of the

Post Office Tower framed between rabbit-hutch office buildings, a darker blue than the sky, and marvelled at how rapidly the silhouette had become part of the London skyscape.

Joining the thick lines of cars making their way inch by inch, she sighed at the long delays. At certain times of day these streets were solidly blocked with traffic and today she was in no mood for sitting in a traffic jam. They moved at a snail's pace while she drummed her fingers on the wheel, but at last she was in Lazreth Square, parking in one of the spaces around the tree-embellished gardens. As she climbed out of her car she remembered suddenly Rob's nostalgic memories of the square and sighed, her face sombre.

Built in the nineteenth century, their four sides made up of terraces of tall, balconied houses with flat frontages, the squares had a characteristic elegance which was the lasting legacy of the period. The central gardens gave them a magic no other London streets possessed. They brought nature into man's working world, reflecting the seasons day by day. In spring their trees burst into bud, the leaves uncoiling inch by inch like bright, curled little hands; in summer a whispering sea of leaves moved on the branches. The paths were criss-crossed with blue-black shadows which shifted in every wind. At lunchtimes, office workers came in to eat their sandwiches on the benches under the trees, throwing crusts to the grey London sparrows which hopped and chirped, dodging the pigeons who fought them for the bread.

Sara crossed the road and walked up the level,

shallow whitewashed steps. As she passed under the portico, supported by smoothly stuccoed columns, a man in a dark brown livery ornamented by polished silver buttons sprang forward to open the door for her.

'Afternoon, miss,' he said politely, 'May I help you?'

'I want to see Mr Rawdon,' Sara said, hoping her nervousness did not show in her face or voice.

The porter surveyed her thoughtfully. 'Have you an appointment, miss?'

She shook her head and saw his face change. 'I'm sorry, miss,' he said. 'Mr Rawdon doesn't see anybody without an appointment.'

Sara almost smiled then because it was fate. She couldn't fight that. Silently, she turned to walk out and the porter stared after her, a frown on his face, his grey hair slipping back· from his pink forehead like a mat on a polished floor.

Sara heard the telephone ring and the porter walked away. She crossed the road and unlocked her car, glancing up briefly at the elegant building she had just left. The porter came running down the steps, waving towards her, but she got into the car and inserted the key into the ignition.

'Miss!' the porter gasped, leaning on her door.

She wound the window down and looked at him expressionlessly.

'Miss,' he panted, 'Mr Rawdon will see you if you come along back inside.'

Sara felt the stiffness of her own smile as she shook her head. 'I've changed my mind,' she said. 'Tell him it doesn't matter.' She started her car and the porter stared down at her, moving back, scratching his head as though puzzled by the oddness of female behaviour.

A large orange van moved in front of her, blocking her exit, and she waited, nervously fingering the wheel. Suddenly Nick was beside the car. The porter stared at him and backed respectfully to give him room to speak to her. Sara stared at the orange van, her chin rigid.

Nick looked at her, his hand on the top of her car, then yanked the door open. She turned, startled, a cry of protest on her lips, and his strong fingers curled round her wrist, pulling her out.

'Let me go, damn you!' she muttered, glaring at him.

He closed the car door with his other hand. 'Keys, Roberts,' he said, throwing her ignition keys to the porter. 'Lock it and keep them until I tell you to give them back.'

'They're my keys,' Sara said furiously.

Nick frogmarched her across the road, his face implacable. 'Don't you dare manhandle me!' she bit out, struggling against his compelling grip.

He pushed her up the steps and into the marble-tiled hall. A clock ticked solemnly on the wall as if to underline the cloistered calm of the place. A woman in a subdued grey dress sat at a wide desk underneath the clock with telephones beside her. She lifted her head to stare as Nick forced Sara struggling across the floor to the lift.

The lift doors slid shut and Nick turned to look

down into her face, his own expressionless.

'What do you think you're doing? I haven't got an appointment, remember, Mr God Almighty!'

The blue eyes flared. 'Be quiet until we're in my office, you maddening little spitfire!'

His office was on the top floor of the building, the corridor smoothly carpeted. Faces lifted as Nick pulled her along beside him into his office. Sara was aware of the stares, the raised eyebrows.

She was thrust inside the room and the door shut. Nick leaned against it, arms folded, breathing heavily.

'I almost broke the four-minute mile getting down there,' he said breathlessly. 'I must be out of condition.

'You needn't have bothered,' she muttered, her face averted.

He laughed curtly. 'The first time you've ever moved towards me of your own free will and you say I shouldn't bother?'

Her face burned. She couldn't look at him.

'Why did you come?' he asked after a pause, his voice now becoming level.

'It doesn't matter.'

'For God's sake,' he brushed it aside. 'It must matter or you wouldn't be here. It is what I said at the Zoo? Did some of it get home?'

She swung round then, her face filled with spitting rage. 'Oh, it got home, Mr Nicholas Rawdon. How dared you talk to me like that? How dare you jump to conclusions about me?'

'You forget, I've personal experience of your

ability to respond,' he snapped, his blue eyes biting into her.

'That works two ways!'

His lips tightened. 'I won't deny it. I've never hidden the fact that I want you, but I draw the line at jumping into bed with everyone who asks.'

'So do I!' Hurt and temper made her voice shake.

He laughed curtly. 'Why lie about it? Don't tell me Forcell hasn't had you—I saw the way he was mooning over you. Not to mention whoever you had at your flat that night.'

'Lucy,' she said fiercely.

He stared. 'What?'

'Lucy, a friend of mine. She was staying with me while her flat was being redecorated.'

For a second she thought he didn't believe that, either, then he shrugged, his hard mouth twisting. 'I suppose Halliday left her behind as a watchdog, did he? He knows you too well to trust you on your own in that flat. That was obvious the night you came to my place.'

Her face was stiff, her eyes coldly angry. 'I'm tired of having you abuse me, Mr Rawdon. I want to get this message home to you once and for all. Greg's not my lover, he's my stepbrother.'

His black brows rose sardonically. 'That old story? You're a bit late with it, aren't you? You've already admitted to me that he's your lover, and the way you ran from my flat that night confirmed his hold over you.'

'I told you what you already believed to stop you trying to seduce me,' Sara bit back contemptuously.

'I had to fend you off somehow. You wouldn't have left me alone if I hadn't.' Her catlike green eyes flashed towards him. 'Now would you? You made that very obvious.'

He didn't move, his eyes on her face. 'The night you came to my flat, when Halliday rang, he threatened to leave you if you didn't go back at once.'

'No,' Sara said forcibly. 'A friend of ours had died. That was what we were talking about, that was what that was all over. Rob had been ill for years, but it was very sudden at the end. Greg was very distressed. But he didn't want me there on his own account, he wanted me to comfort Rob's wife. Greg loves Lucy deeply, but he couldn't cope with her grief. He is too involved. It tore him apart to see her so unhappy.'

'He doesn't love you?' Nick sounded shaken, his voice rough.

Sara met his eyes, her own filled with anger and contempt. 'No, Greg doesn't love me, not that way. He and I are very close, but there's no romantic feeling between us. I suppose Greg is a cross between father and brother to me, and I'm a mixture of daughter and sister to him.'

Nick took a step towards her, his face dark. 'You couldn't keep your eyes off him the night we met.'

'He was woried sick about Lucy and he was drinking. Of course I watched him. I feel responsible for him. He feels responsible for me.'

'You're hung-up on him,' Nick muttered. 'You always have been.'

Fierce rage almost split her head open. She

looked at him with sparks shooting from the vivid green eyes.

'I might as well have saved my breath. You prefer your own version of the truth, don't you? Just don't come near me again. I never want to set eyes on you for the rest of my life. I won't be labelled as a tramp, Mr Rawdon. In future keep your filthy thoughts to yourself!'

As she moved to thrust past him, he caught at her arm, bending to say urgently, 'Wait, Sara.'

She knocked his hand away, turning a blind, furious face towards him. 'Don't touch me!'

His secretary stood outside the door, a large grey folder in her hand. As Sara swung open the door and walked out the woman sidestepped to avoid her. Sara moved towards the corridor and all the heads lifted again to stare. Nick brushed aside his secretary with a set expression and strode after Sara.

The lift had just arrived at the floor as Sara ran towards it. The doors slid open and a woman got out. Sara hardly glanced at her, moving very fast, but she got the impression of curious, staring eyes. Nick was leaping towards her as she jumped into the lift. The doors began to close and the woman who had just left the lift said sharply, 'Nick?' as his lean body dived towards Sara.

Nick halted for a second, long enough for the doors to shut. Sara stood there, breathing rapidly, shaking. When she got to the marble-tiled hall she asked the porter for her keys. His pink forehead gleamed as he smiled uncertainly at her.

'Mr Rawdon will give them to you, miss.' His

eye passed over her shoulder and she looked back too, seeing the light travel above the lift. Nick was in that lift, she thought. She turned and ran out of the bank. A taxi was cruising past. She pulled open the door and the driver looked round at her. She gave her address and he nodded. The taxi pulled away just as Nick dived down the steps and stopped short on the pavement, gazing after them.

She didn't need to think twice about what she was going to do. Nick had her car and she knew he would follow her to her flat. She leaned forward and gave the driver fresh instructions. He dropped her at Lucy's flat and she sat on the doorstep until Lucy puffed up the stairs and stopped dead, staring at her.

'What are you doing here?'

'Waiting for you,' Sara said drily, standing.

Lucy slid the key into the lock, eyeing her. 'You look ghastly. Oh, Sara, what's wrong? Something is, I can tell that. You look the way you did the night you fainted.'

'Before you ring Greg, I am not, repeat not, pregnant,' Sara said with a grim smile.

Lucy's colour rose. 'I didn't say you were. I wouldn't make the same mistake twice.'

'Then you're superhuman,' Sara muttered bitterly. 'I wish to God I could say the same.'

Lucy moved to the little kitchen. 'Are you hungry? Can I get you something to eat?'

Sara perched on the tall kitchen stool, her slender body draped gracefully on it, her red hair gleaming. Lucy eyed her as she moved about.

'You and Greg are both so secretive,' she complained.

'I could eat some toast,' Sara countered, knowing that that would sidetrack Lucy, who had a passion for feeding people, looking after them.

While she was making the toast Lucy said: 'You don't eat enough, either you or Greg. Thin as rails, both of you.'

'Greg needs looking after,' Sara agreed. 'I try to get him to eat properly, but he forgets once he has started work.'

Lucy smiled and then turned away, the fine drift of her dark hair hiding her face.

'Can I stay here tonight?' Sara asked, her head bent as she began to nibble at the toast she did not really want. Her stomach was heaving. The tension of her interview with Nick still hung over her and the last thing she wanted to do was eat, but she somehow forced herself to do it.

'Of course,' Lucy said at once, but she stared, her face filled with curiosity. She was dying to ask further questions, but she knew better than to hope Sara would answer them. Lucy knew how secretive Greg and Sara were about their private lives, their feelings, and she had learnt to respect their refusal to discuss those things.

She leant over to remove the toast Sara was trying hard to swallow. 'You don't really want that, do you? I don't know what's wrong, but it won't do you any good to eat when you feel sick.'

Sara laughed wryly. 'How did you guess?'

Lucy eyed her with rueful amusement. 'Look in a mirror.'

Sara did so, later, and was horrified by the expression on her own face, the pallor and tension, the shadows under her eyes. Her normal vivacity had gone, leaving a mask she did not recognise. Nick Rawdon was having a catastrophic effect on her.

She did not sleep very well that night although she tried to lie still so as not to disturb Lucy, whose sleep pattern was just adjusting after her long grief for Rob.

Sara went back to her flat next morning and found her car parked outside. The car keys were on her mat. Beside them lay a note from Nick asking her to ring him at the bank. 'I must speak to you,' it said. She tore it up and started work with a set expression on her face.

That afternoon the telephone rang. She answered it absently and Nick said huskily, 'Sara, I must speak to you.'

She put the telephone down without answering. As she turned away it rang again and she took it off the hook and left it off.

She heard his car roar up the road an hour later. Standing in the room she listened to his footsteps, the prolonged ringing of the bell. He went round the side of the house, as he had before, but Sara had locked up very carefully. She quietly slipped upstairs into Greg's flat and tried to ignore Nick's insistent ringing and knocking.

He rang again that night. She couldn't leave the

telephone off the hook for ever. 'Stop ringing,' she said fiercely. 'Or I'll have to move out of here. I don't want to speak to you. I never want to see you again in my life!'

The crash of her receiver must have deafened him. It must also have got the message home. He did not ring again, nor did he come to her home.

She was glad about that, relieved, and the only reason why she felt like crying all the time was because she hated him. Every time she looked into a mirror she remembered to hate him because it was him who had put those shadows under her eyes, given a new fine-drawn tension to her face.

She did not want to see him. She did not ever want to set eyes on him again. They were chalk and cheese, separated by deeply entrenched attitudes bred by their different upbringings, with nothing in common. They disagreed on almost everything, argued, quarrelled, fought. All that they had was based on a physical attraction which dragged them together whenever they met, but that was no basis for a serious relationship.

She forced herself to work harder than ever because that helped to shut him out and whenever she could she visited Lucy and kept talking to her about Greg, doing what little she could to improve Greg's chances, hoping that one of them, at least, could salvage something from the stupid wreckage of their emotional lives.

Greg came back from France very brown and thinner than ever, his eyes carefully controlled when he first met Lucy, avoiding a direct glance at her.

Lucy was very flushed that first time. She, too, could not look at Greg, but gradually the stiffness seeped out of her and she forgot Greg's feelings as she made the elaborate meal she had planned for his first evening home.

She was so pleased by her success with the meal that she laughed as Greg plaintively complained that he could barely move afterwards. Sara caught her breath as Lucy allowed Greg to help her wash up. Discreetly she slid off and left them together. It wasn't going to be easy for Greg. He would have a long, long wait, but she sensed that one day he would get his wish.

Greg insisted on taking both her and Lucy to the ballet one evening. The tickets had been sent to him by someone he had painted for, and he was lucky to get them, because it was hard to get tickets for the ballet during the summer season.

Sara had a new dress for the occasion, a simple little white thing that gave her skin a glimmering pallor, throwing the blaze of her hair into dramatic relief. Lucy was excited, for once flushed as Greg seated her, smiling at him eagerly. Greg picked up her programme for the third time as she dropped it, laughing at her, and Sara gazed absently around at the throng of faces.

In a box on the other side of the theatre she saw Nick, her eyes widening before she hurriedly looked away. He was studying his own programme, his black head bent, and the beautiful woman beside him was talking to him with the concentrated attention Nick always got from women, her eyes fixed on his hard profile in apparent rapture.

Sara glanced towards the box again as the lights went down and saw Nick's outline in a black silhouette, her heart aching as though it was being crushed.

His companion was ravishing, her evening gown glinting in the light as she moved, the white shoulders enhanced by the diamond necklace she wore. During the interval Sara risked a glance at him again, catching him laughing at something his companion said, his face in amused relief against his white and gilt chair.

Suddenly he turned his head in a restless movement, his eyes sweeping round the theatre. Sara abruptly bent to pick up her own programme from the floor.

She did not want him to see her. She sensed he had not yet done so and she wanted to keep it that way. She fumbled blindly on the floor and Greg looked down, frowning. 'What's wrong?'

Sara picked up her programme and slowly uncoiled. 'Nothing,' she said, hoping the flush of her face would be taken for the natural result of bending down for too long.

She did not look at Nick, but some buried instinct warned her that he had now seen her. She stared at the gilded crowns on the curtain and a slow prickle passed down her spine. Without turning her head his way she managed to sneak a sidelong glance towards the box. Nick was leaning on the velvet parapet with opera glasses in his hands, his eyes fixed on her.

Greg leaned towards her, offering her a chocolate from the box he had bought as they entered the theatre. Sara took a long time choosing one, aware of Greg's perplexed stare.

'Are you hot?' he asked. 'You're very flushed.'

'No,' she lied.

Greg put the back of his hand against her cheek. 'What do you mean, no? You're burning!'

'It's stuffy in here,' she said. 'Don't you think so, Lucy?'

Lucy leaned across Greg, frowning. 'I hadn't noticed.' Greg glanced at her, his brows lifted, and Lucy shrugged at him in a silent exchange which Sara vaguely noted.

The curtain went up again, the house lights were lowered, and music stole softly up towards them. Sara slipped a look towards Nick's box and hurriedly away again. He was still watching her, his opera glasses trained on her, apparently oblivious to what was happening on the stage. Sara saw the movement of his companion's hand in the darkness, her tap on Nick's arm, the swing of his black head and the slow lowering of his opera glasses.

He did not turn to look at Sara again, but she sat stiffly, watching the dancers without seeing them, the wreathed and stylised convolutions of their movement like the flickering of white shadows to her, the music passing through her head in ironic counterpoint to her own emotions.

Seeing Nick had brought home to her the depth of her love for him, the stupid wasted emotions he had aroused in her. She could have sat all night untiringly watching that dark profile. She wanted to cry, but she didn't. She sat with a faint, painted smile on her lips and hoped she was pulling the wool over everyone's eyes, afraid though that Greg, at least, was not fooled by her cheerful air.

A movement in Nick's box attracted her attention. She saw him lean over, his white shirt-front standing out in the dark box, and imagined him touching the woman with him, perhaps kissing her. Why else had he moved? Jealousy twisted down inside her like a vicious corkscrew.

She looked at the stage again, dazed to find the ballet finishing. Applause broke out. The ritual of curtain clamour, the flowers, the bows and smiles and hand-kissing. Sara watched it like a zombie and wouldn't let herself glance again at Nick.

Greg led Lucy and Sara along the crowded aisle towards the exit and all around Sara voices rose in bright comment on the dancing, the orchestra. She felt oddly isolated, cold. Greg looked back over his shoulder, frowning, and she summoned another of her false, bright smiles.

They pushed their way down into the packed foyer. Sara looked at Greg's back as she followed him. She did not want to look elsewhere in case she found herself looking at Nick. She was tensely concentrating now on getting out of there without another painful encounter.

He would be with his beautiful companion, of course. He'd have no time to look aside at Sara tonight. Perhaps he had already erased her memory, crossed her off his list. Why had he ever pursued her in the first place with women like that on his visiting list? Sara did not need to pause to compare herself with the woman who had sat in the box with him. Even that brief glimpse of her had been enough to tell Sara that in looks, clothes, manner, the other woman had outshone her on every point.

Women like that came from Nick's world, the moneyed class to which he belonged. Sara was outside all that and did not regret it for a second.

As they finally pushed out into the cool night air Greg moved off to hail one of the waiting taxis and Lucy bent to fiddle with her shoe strap. Sara stood there, numbly looking at the stars in the London sky. They seemed oddly out of place up there, their light doused by the brilliance of the street lights below.

'Sara,' said a voice. A hand touched her arm.

She froze, her head turned away. Greg waved and Lucy, unaware of anything but that, said cheerfully, 'Oh, good, he's got a taxi. Come on!'

Sara moved jerkily forward after Lucy's hurrying figure. Nick's hand held her back, gripping her arm.

'Let me go,' she muttered, still not looking at him.

His hand dropped. Sara walked away and didn't look back.

CHAPTER EIGHT

In middle June the weather moved into a dazzling heatwave, the skies a burning blue day after day, the London streets filled with a baking warmth which radiated from the pavements as one walked. Sara was feeling oddly tired most of the time, unable to work, spending her days doing so little that Greg regarded her with anxiety whenever he saw her.

'You don't look well,' he told her, and she brushed aside the remark with a quick pretence of a smile.

'I'm fine.'

It was her constant cry these days. Lucy was as worried as Greg and got the same reply. She would not have anyone suspect how miserable she was, it would have added another dimension to her unhappiness for either Greg or Lucy to know how she felt.

She was glad when a commission arrived suddenly from some woman in Kent who wanted a landscape painted of her garden. It would get her out of London, remove her from Nick's milieu and from the quiet appraisal of Greg's too shrewd eyes.

Greg went off to Cambridgeshire the same day, as it happened, so Lucy moved into Sara's flat for a while to look after the garden for her, and Sara drove down to Kent with a determination to forget Nick Rawdon.

The house to which she was going was called

Heronbrook and lay in the rolling downlands of Kent which run down to the sea. Mrs Walters had given her clear directions in her letter.

She found Heronbrook easily enough. It lay well back from a narrow country road in a sheltered position and when she had parked outside it Sara sat in her car inspecting the house with interest. It was neither grand nor small, a large family house built, she would guess, in the 1920s with pale yellow continental shutters on the white walls beside the windows, and a sunny air of being very much loved.

When she rang the doorbell, the front door was opened by a middle-aged woman in a dark blue dress who gave Sara a long stare from eyes which had the washed-out blue of a March sky. Tall, gaunt, with a long, horse-like face, she radiated hostility. Sara looked at her in surprised bewilderment, wondering if the woman disliked artists on principle. She had met people like that.

'Come in,' the woman said with pale compressed lips, when Sara had announced her identity.

Sara came, torn between amusement and irritation. She followed the woman through a hall panelled in pale golden oak, the tiny pleats of her pale green dress whirling around her slender legs as she walked.

'Miss Nichols,' the woman said very loudly, almost as though in accusation, glaring at whoever sat in the room.

Sara walked into the room with a polite smile and stopped dead as she recognised the woman who was getting up from a velvet armchair.

Nick's sister looked at her with the charming smile she had seen in the photograph in his flat. Her hand was extended as she moved towards Sara. 'I'm so glad you've come,' she said, and then, seeing the way Sara's eyes flicked nervously round the room, she said, 'No, Nick isn't here.'

Giving her a look of shock, Sara slowly accepted her hand, and Judith smiled at her. 'Come and sit down. You look shattered.'

Sara sat because she couldn't have stood a second longer. Her legs were trembling. She glanced round the pleasant room and then back to the other woman, a disturbed question in her green eyes.

Judith glanced at the woman who had let Sara in. 'You can bring in the tea, Tilly.'

'I don't like it,' the older woman retorted, settling her hands at her waist. Her enormous teeth showed as she spoke. They gave gloom a head start, making the horse-like face permanently depressed.

'Nobody asked you to like it. Go and get the tea.'

Sara stared at them both, wondering about the relationship between them. She had thought as she was shown in that the older woman was a servant, but now she wondered. There was a confidence about the way Tilly spoke back to Judith that made her ask herself if they were related.

'And what will you say when Nick finds out?' Tilly demanded with a rough voice.

'Tilly, mind your own business!'

Judith sounded as though she might lose her temper at any moment. Tilly gave her a long, fulminating look, then turned without another word and disappeared with the walk of a stiff-legged stork, her left foot dragging behind her.

'Oh, dear,' Judith wailed. 'She's limping.'

Sara was startled enough to ask: 'Has she hurt her foot?'

'She sprained it ten years ago, but there's nothing wrong with it now. Nick had our doctor go over it with a slide rule and he assured us it was perfectly sound. All the same, when Tilly's mad, she limps.'

'Why is she mad?' Sara asked, leaning back in the comfortable green velvet chair.

Judith eyed her. 'She doesn't approve of what I'm doing.'

Her green eyes on the other's face, Sara asked quietly, 'And what are you doing? Why am I here, Mrs Waters?'

'Judith, please call me Judith.' The pleasant face broke into a smile which was half amused, half placatory. 'I brought you down to meet you, to be frank, and to see if there was anything I could do.'

Sara sat up straight. 'About what?'

Her crisp tone made Judith grimace. 'Don't be cross, please. I've had enough of that from Nick. He's never been what I'd call a sweet-tempered soul, but in the last year he's become unbearable. Tilly and I knew there was somebody, but we couldn't find out who. Then I saw him with you at the zoo that day and of course I knew, although I still didn't know who you were. Nick wouldn't say a word. He can be maddeningly secretive at times.'

'How did you find out my name?' Sara couldn't help asking that.

'Well ...' Judith was rather pink. 'Rather disgracefully, I'm afraid. That's another reason Tilly's furious with me. I stayed the weekend at Nick's flat the week before last and while he was out I looked through his private desk.'

Sara's eyes rounded. 'I'm afraid I agree with Tilly, that was rather disgraceful of you.' She loved Greg dearly, but she would never pry into his private life like that.

Judith's chin firmed. 'All the same, it told me what I wanted to know. I found a tiny cutting folded into a drawer by itself. It was a newspaper photograph of you at some exhibition with a painter and it gave your name, so I found out who you were and what you did. The rest was easy. I rang round until I got your address and I wrote to you.'

Sara pleated her skirt, her bright red head bent. 'I appreciate your concern for your brother, but I'm afraid you've got the wrong idea. There's nothing between Mr Rawdon and myself.'

'Oh, fiddlesticks!' Judith retorted.

Sara looked up, flushed. 'I assure you ...'

'You can tell me until you're blue in the face, but I know my brother and I've never seen him look the way he does now.'

Sara's breath caught harshly. 'How does he look?' The moment the question came out she wished she hadn't asked, but a bright gleam of triumph came into Judith's eyes.

'As sick as a dog,' she said, and Sara was torn between laughter and pain.

'I wasn't sitting back with my hands folded while

Nick went around in a permanent rotten, lousy temper,' said Judith, and the door opened and Tilly dragged in, pushing a trolley.

'Nice words for one of the boys to hear,' she observed, giving Judith a fierce look which moved on disapprovingly to Sara.

'They can't hear me,' Judith argued.

'They might, and then we know what would happen. They'd start using words like that and their father wouldn't like it. I'd be the one to get blamed, I've no doubt.'

She began to pour out tea, her hands large and capable. 'Is she staying, then? If she'd any sense she'd drive straight back to London.'

'You are staying, aren't you?' Judith appealed to Sara.

'I can't.' Sara muttered the words without looking at her.

'He won't thank you for it,' Tilly informed Judith, handing her a cup and then passing one to Sara.

'I'm not asking him to,' Judith snapped. 'Go away, Tilly, and mind your own business, as you won't help.'

'Nick is my business, always has been since he was in nappies, and he's going to be livid when he knows what you've done.' The grim tones sounded as though Tilly contemplated that with pleasure. The pale eyes swivelled to Sara, sparkling wrath in them. 'She doesn't want him. Leave it alone.'

Sara leapt to her feet, almost spilling the tea. 'Really, I can't discuss this with you. I must go.'

Judith caught her hand, held it tightly. 'Please, just stay for tea. Talk to me. Nick isn't here, I promise you. Oh, Tilly, go away! You're ruining everything.' She stamped her foot like an infuriated child and Tilly looked at her haughtily.

'Hoity-toity. Very well, go ahead, but don't come crying to me when Nick finds out.' She slammed the door as she went and Judith subsided.

'Please, sit down again and drink your tea.'

Sara reluctantly sat. 'But I refuse to talk about Nick,' she warned with her eyes on her cup.

Judith offered her a square plate of tiny sandwiches and Sara found herself automatically taking one although she found it hard to swallow a morsel, her throat so dry it felt as if it was full of ashes.

'How long would it take you to paint our stream?' Judith asked brightly.

'I can't,' Sara said roughly. 'It's impossible, you must see that.'

'I'm not asking the impossible,' Judith said with a slight smile. 'I just want you to stay for a while, let me get to know you.'

Sara looked up. 'Why?'

'Please,' Judith pleaded. 'I swear I'm not expecting Nick. You must see that he doesn't know you're here, and he'll be at work during the week. He wouldn't come down without letting me know.'

Sara concentrated on her plate, the half-eaten little sandwich. 'You're off course,' she said with difficulty. 'Nick isn't seriously interested in me.'

'Are you in him?' Judith asked quickly.

After a second's hesitation Sara lied, 'No.'

'Then where's the problem if you stay and paint our garden?' Judith asked with bright triumph.

Sara looked up wryly. 'You're almost as stubborn as your brother,' she remarked.

'He is, isn't he?' Judith agreed. 'Pigheaded. I did admire you for slapping his face that day. I always used to want to hit him, but he was so much bigger than me when we were children, and he had no scruples about hitting back.'

'I thought he was going to hit me,' Sara admitted, half smiling.

'So did I,' Judith nodded. 'Heavens, he was in a temper for the rest of the day! Even the boys were nervous of him and he's usually quite patient with them; even when Andrew broke Nick's old cricket bat, which he'd treasured since he was in the school team, Nick only growled a bit.'

'Is Andrew the eldest?'

Judith needed no further invitation. She had a large leather-covered album on Sara's lap a moment later and was seated on the arm of her chair showing her endless photographs of small, dark boys with mischievous eyes and vulnerable little bodies.

'Andrew looks rather like Nick did at that age,' Judith told her, showing her a faded old snapshot at which Sara peered with fascinated interest. Nick at seven with a skinny body and a banana grin seemed appealingly-poignant to her. 'Now Patrick looks like my husband, David, which is rather worrying because David's beginning to thin out on top. I do hope he isn't going bald.'

Sara looked at the photo of the boys' father, his

calm amused face as he watched his sons. He looked older than Judith, around forty-five, Sara decided.

'He's in Mexico,' Judith sighed. 'A business trip. I hate it when he's away for weeks, but I can't go with him because that means leaving the children alone for too long. They drive Tilly mad.'

She glanced at her small silver wristwatch. 'They should be back soon. I've got a Swiss au pair who's taken them for a walk.'

'Does Tilly look after the house?'

Judith nodded. 'She'd leave me like a shot and move in with Nick if he'd have her, but he's got the Firths and when Tilly hints, Nick always says I need her more. Much Tilly cares. Nick always was her favourite.'

'She's been with you a long time?'

'All my life and nearly all of Nick's,' Judith agreed. 'Now she runs this house and keeps us all in order. I wish she'd go to Nick, but Nick's no fool.'

Sara laughed. 'I'm sure you're fond of her.'

'Of course I am,' Judith sighed. 'But she's a domestic tyrant. Luckily she adores Nicola. A stroke of genius calling her after Nick, wasn't it? Tilly at once fell for her like a ton of bricks. I love babies, but they are tiring and it's such a relief that Tilly will condescend to have Nicola around some of the day.' Suddenly she got up. 'Let me show you your room. I picked out the nicest one in the house. It has a super view.'

Sara followed, protesting. 'Look, really, I don't think ...'

'Please,' Judith said with a smile. 'It can't do any

harm, can it? I really would like to get to know you and I'd love one of your pictures.'

Sara followed her up the wide staircase and exclaimed with pleasure over the large, sunny room she had been given. Judith left her with her suitcase to unpack and vanished to deal with her returning children, whose stamps and loud cries came floating up the stairs.

Sara unpacked and stowed all her things away, then stood at the window looking over the green gardens. The afternoon was fading into a rose and blue twilight which gave the view the effect of a stained glass window, tranquil and soft.

A dragging sound alerted her and she looked round at Tilly's horse face. 'Can you eat kidneys?' Tilly demanded, as though daring her to deny it.

'I can eat almost anything,' Sara said.

'Well, that's a mercy because that's all there is tonight. Nick's been off his food for months.' The pale eyes accused her.

Sara felt hot colour flood into her face, and said nothing.

'I'm not nosy, like Judith,' Tilly informed her offendedly. 'But I don't like it when he's off his food.'

'Shouldn't you discuss this with him, not me?' Sara asked coldly.

'He wouldn't tell me if I did.'

'Maybe he doesn't want you to know,' Sara said tartly.

'No maybe about it,' Tilly muttered. 'Always a difficult child. You don't think that stops me wondering, do you?'

'Wonder all you like,' said Sara, grinning suddenly, the vitality and warmth of her smile catching Tilly unaware.

The washed-out eyes narrowed. 'Hmm,' Tilly said nastily. 'How old are you?'

'Twenty-four,' Sara told her. 'My parents are dead, I live in London and I've got all my own teeth.' She showed them, her smile barbed, and Tilly gazed at her.

'Saucy, aren't you? I can imagine you've been giving Nick a hard time.'

Sara bit back a blistering reply, her face closing up.

Tilly nodded, the movement of her lips over her teeth passing for a smile. 'I know what you're like, just looking at that red hair. A hot-tempered madam, aren't you?'

Sara gave her a cold look, her eyes biting. 'You know nothing about me. Kindly mind your own business.'

Tilly's smile widened and got nastier. 'A little firework, spitting and bouncing all over the place. No wonder Nick got his fingers burnt!'

Sara walked past her with her head held high and Tilly limped after her, chuckling to herself. Evil old witch, Sara thought, how dare she talk to me like that?

Her view of Tilly altered gradually over the next week as she painted in the sunny, spacious garden. She saw a good deal of Judith and the children, but she saw more of Tilly, who took to walking down to the stream to stand and make rude comments about her work. Sara got mad at first but gradually found herself laughing, almost waiting with eagerness for Tilly's dry remarks. They always held the germ of truth, although they were often muttered so gruffly that they disguised the real value of their content. The more she saw of the old woman the more she was amused by her. Tilly was an original, blunt to the point of insult yet with warmth beneath the sharp gritty surface.

Judith was quite a different proposition. She was a poised, confident woman some ten years Sara's senior, smoothly groomed, charming, very friendly. Sara liked her, but she found herself far more eager to talk to Tilly. Some of those barbed little digs were so funny that Sara treasured them to repeat them to Greg, who would also, she felt, find Tilly funny.

Tilly questioned her sharply about her life, listened with obvious interest. 'This Greg, then,' she said. 'Lives with you, you say?'

'He's my stepbrother, and yes, he lives in the same house. We have a flat each.'

Tilly eyed her. 'Not married, then?'

'Not yet,' said Sara, half smiling as she thought hopefully of Lucy.

'Planning to?' Tilly asked, and Sara found herself telling her the story of Lucy and Rob. Tilly looked sadly at her.

'There then, that was a bad blow. I had a brother once, died of something like that.' While Sara was off guard, nodding to that remark, Tilly asked, 'Nick jealous, was he?'

Sara looked up, her face flooding with colour. She didn't answer, hurriedly looking away. Tilly wandered off, grinning.

The hot June days drifted like dandelion clocks, blowing softly through the green meadows surrounding the house, giving the garden a tranced and idyllic grace. Sara watched the boys building a dam in the stream, laughing as it broke up and washed along the bank, sending twigs and rich mud into the reeds. Mallards rose in angry protest as the water washed by them and the boys ran off giggling, their feet filthy and their faces sun-flushed.

In her lobsterpot playpen, Nicola waved her fingers at the birds as they flew past, bubbling softly as she practised her one word. 'Dadda, Dadda,' she said all day, untiring and contented, her plump brown arms dimpled at the elbow, her broderie anglaise sunbonnet hiding the tufts of dark hair which gave her a comic look of her uncle. It always took Sara aback to see Nick's fierce blue eyes in that rounded little face. Judith was not far off when she said the baby looked like him and Sara suspected the resemblance would become more marked as Nicola got older.

The sun was so hot that Tilly marched down with an old straw hat she had unearthed and jammed it down over Sara's bright curls.

'Get sunstroke, you will,' she muttered. 'Now, keep it on!'

Sara grimaced at her back as she left. Tilly was more and more showing a tendency to domineer over her, governing her as she governed Judith and the children. Sara could see that everything within the orbit of Heronbrook was Tilly's property and, in a sense, it was flattering that Tilly should have decided to add her to her possessions, but at the same time it was maddening. Sara was too used to independence to find it amusing to be treated as a little girl again, yet saucy though Tilly might describe her, Sara didn't have the stomach to fight Tilly. Her own growing fondness for the older woman had softened her. Struggling, she was already submitting to that domestic tyranny which Judith groaned over in private. There were tyrants and tyrants, Sara thought grimly, and the worst was love, because somehow one could not fight it. Under Tilly's gloomy exterior, her sharp pronouncements, lay a love which weakened all opposition.

Sucking her brush handle, Sara pushed the hat back over her vibrant hair to survey the rippling water. It was testing her technical ability to paint the stream. Water was always difficult.

Voices drifted down to her and she turned absently to get a shock as she saw Nick. He was standing on the slope above her with Annabel Forcell and Jeremy with Judith in anxious attendance on them all, but for that first moment Sara only saw Nick. He stood there in a pale beige denim suit, his darker shirt open at the throat, the bare brown skin gleaming in the sunlight, his face stupefied.

There was no other word for it, Sara thought, seeing his expression. For a second she had been stupefied herself, so she knew the feeling, but as she took in his staggered face she started to laugh, amused, and the astonishment went out of his blue eyes to be replaced by rage, pure and simple rage.

Jeremy was moving towards her, both hands extended. 'Darling, what are you doing here?'

She stood up and let him take her hands, leaning back to smile up at him vividly, her slanting eyes filled with amusement. 'What does it look like?'

Annabel had strolled down. 'You get around, don't you?' There was cold hostility in her voice. Sara saw from her petulant face that Annabel had not forgotten the evening of her party, when Sara left taking Nick with her.

Nick joined them, his hands jammed into his pockets. He glanced at her easel, then at the stream. His blue gaze glittered as it shot to his sister. Judith had a transparent air of innocence, her face bland.

'I've rung several times, but you're never in,' Jeremy complained. 'It's wonderful to see you again.'

'It's nice to see you,' she smiled sweetly, and Jeremy pulled on her hands to draw her nearer and kiss her lightly.

'Isn't it hot down here?' Judith fanned herself dramatically. 'How can you stand it?'

'Tilly's found me a hat.' Sara tilted her head in it, her green eyes mischievous. 'Do you think it suits me? I feel I should be breaking into a soft shoe shuffle!'

The hat was old and discoloured, the straw brim bent, but somehow on the small bright head it was provocative and Jeremy's eyes brightened with admiration.

'Very pretty,' he said, and Sara flicked a brief glance at Nick through her lashes. He was looking at her, but he moved his eyes away and stared at the distant green fields beyond the garden.

'I somehow got the idea you were in France with your brother,' Jeremy commented.

Nick turned his head quickly and looked back at her.

'Greg's home now,' Sara answered. 'He's gone up to Cambridgeshire to see a horse.'

'Why don't we all go in and have tea?' Judith asked brightly, not quite meeting Nick's cold gaze.

Sara walked beside Jeremy, her slight curved body casual in the blue shorts and tiny blue sun-top she was wearing. The shorts were denim, very brief, the brevity giving new length to her brown legs.

The tea party was difficult. Nick wasn't saying a thing, lounging in his chair with a cold look on his face, barely glancing at Sara. Annabel was talking to him, though. She talked throughout the meal, bright eager remarks to which Nick barely replied. Judith passed tea and food, looked amused and, whenever she accidentally met her brother's eyes, slightly nervous. She was hiding it well, though. Jeremy seemed blind to the atmosphere. He concentrated on Sara, leaning towards her, laughing, talking about his father, Ravens Halt, the picture she had painted, the weather. He passed from one topic to another with barely a pause and Sara listened as though fascinated, her green eyes on his face, smiling at him.

When they had exhausted all the topics Jeremy could dredge up, and the tea was gone, Sara deliberately started talking about the picture she was painting. Jeremy listened with the same interest she had shown him, his eyes on her face, watching the vivid mobility of it as she spoke. Sara could sense Nick's irritation, see the drumming of his fingers on the arm of his chair.

Annabel tried to engage him in conversation again, but Nick merely nodded to her chatter, his brows black above the angry blue eyes.

Suddenly the party began breaking up. Nick rose, very tall, his skin taut over his bones, the lines of his mouth set in a cold look.

'If you're going to get back to town, you should be setting off,' he said to Jeremy.

Jeremy rose, obedient to the flick of the master's whip. 'Yes, sir,' he responded like a good and faithful dog, but his eyes stole back to Sara.

He opened his mouth to speak and Nick took his arm, his hand closing round it, almost shoving him towards the door. Annabel followed with her mouth turned down. The look she gave Sara as she went was sulky. Judith went with them, talking brightly, but over her shoulder she gave Sara the look of someone saluting before a battle.

Sara looked at the tea and leaned over to pick up the last tiny white-iced domino cake which Jeremy had been grazing on during the tea. Tilly had made them that afternoon. They were delicious. She bit into it, lying back in her chair, waiting.

She heard Nick's voice in the hall five minutes later. He was speaking icily to Judith, but she couldn't hear what he was saying. She got the message from his tone, however. Nick was flaying his sister. His tone had a metallic, biting ring to it.

Sara held the little cake and took another small

bite. Judith was hardly saying a word, she noted. Nick was doing all the talking. She wondered what he was saying.

Stretching her long golden-brown legs, she stared at the sky through the window. It was a blue so halcyon, so meltingly tender, it moved one to tears, the dark shadows of the trees drifting across it as they shifted in the light breeze.

Behind her the door opened. She did not look round. Languidly she put the cake to her mouth and finished it, dusting her fingers of the clinging crumbs.

She felt Nick's gaze on her. He stood there for a moment, then the door slammed shut and she heard him walk forward.

'I'm sorry if my sister has embarrassed you with all this,' he said stiffly beside her.

Sara was taken aback. She had somehow expected him to storm at her, the way he had just been attacking Judith.

To give herself time to think, she stretched lazily, the movement the sensual, sleepy stretch of a cat in the sun, her arms curved above her head, her slim body graceful.

Nick was staring. She felt his eyes fixed on her, but she didn't look round.

'Judith hasn't embarrassed me,' she shrugged. 'I was glad of the work.'

There was a long silence from him. 'Why did you come?' he asked huskily.

'I told you—I need the work.'

He moved to the window and stood with his back

to her, his shoulders stiff. 'You know what I mean. You wouldn't speak to me on the phone, you ignored me the night I saw you at the ballet. Why did you come down here to Judith's?'

Sara regarded his lean body, her eyes half closed. 'I didn't know who she was until I got here,' she murmured.

He drew in his breath sharply. 'I see.' He laughed shortly. 'I should have worked that out.'

He turned slowly and Sara at once looked away, her face slightly flushed.

'But will you listen to me now?' he asked in a voice she had never heard him use before, his eyes fixed on her.

The door opened and Tilly came dragging in, limping violently. 'Can I clear the tea things now?'

Nick's muttered word made her stare at him, baring her teeth in affront. 'You watch your language, Nick. Don't you look at me like that either. Are you staying? There's no suitcase in your car. Why didn't you let us know you were coming? How many times do I have to tell you that you can't just drop in out of the blue for meals?'

'Oh, hell and damnation!' Nick flung as he stalked out of the room, slamming the door after him.

CHAPTER NINE

TILLY gave Sara a grim nod, as if to say 'I told you so,' and began to clear the tea things dexterously.

'Delicious cakes,' Sara flattered her. It did her no good. Tilly merely gave her one of her dry little smiles.

'I told you he'd be angry.'

'Nice to be right every time,' Sara retorted.

'You can watch your tongue too,' Tilly informed her. 'You're too quick with it even if you don't swear like Nick.'

She left, no longer dragging her foot, and a few minutes later Judith appeared, sneaking a quick look to make sure Sara was alone. 'Whew!' she exclaimed, sinking on to the couch. 'Talk about temper! He was giving off blue sparks!'

'What did you say to him?'

'I didn't,' Judith assured her. 'I let him do all the talking, and Nick can talk when he likes. He never repeated himself once, but he said enough to make me feel two inches high. Am I glad I don't work for him—he must be murder in the bank!' She turned to eye Sara hopefully. 'Has he spoken to you yet?'

'Tilly came in before he'd said much,' Sara told her.

Judith grimaced. 'Trust Tilly! I hope to God I haven't done all this for nothing.'

Sara got up. 'I'm going back to get on with my picture.'

Judith looked alarmed. 'Don't leave me alone with him.'

'Sorry,' Sara retorted without mercy. 'You'll have to face the music, I'm afraid. I expect he'll get over it but as Tilly said, you knew the risks you ran.'

She left Judith wailing and wandered down through the sunny garden to her easel. Tilly had removed Nicola and her playpen from the grass. The boys had vanished, too, no doubt to be bathed before being put to bed. The afternoon was gliding softly into a muted twilight, gilding the water with a last beauty before the sun sank for the night.

Sara stared across the stream, watching a wren who had built a nest on the far side, the tiny body darting in a zigzag flight to hide its destination from prying eyes.

Sara began to touch in flake white, her brow concentrated, trying not to think of the strange way Nick had looked at her before Tilly came in to interrupt them.

Nick came down the garden so softly that she didn't hear him until he suddenly loomed beside her, his black head way above hers, so that she had to tilt the straw hat to look at him in surprise.

The sight of him brought hot colour into her face, but Nick looked calmer now, his face completely under control.

'I realise you don't want to hear what I have to say,' he began at once in level tones. 'But let me say it.'

She glanced away, her eyes moving back to her canvas, and Nick made a rough sound of impatience.

'Forget that.'

'I can listen while I work,' she retorted.

He took the brush from her, dropped it on her stool and seized her arm in tight fingers. She stood in his grip, her head bent down, the wind rustling her hair around the straw brim of the hat.

'Why did you let me go on believing what I did?' he burst out suddenly. 'Did it amuse you? Was it one of your peculiar games, another tease?'

'You were having so much fun calling me a cheap little tramp,' she replied tartly.

'You can't believe that! You knew what you were doing to me.'

'Your mind was made up about me from the start!' Sara flung at him angrily.

'I haven't got a mind,' he muttered. 'You drove me out of it long ago.'

She felt her heart thud violently. She stared down at the grass on which they stood, the crushed scent of it coming up to her, sweet and warm and pungent.

'That doesn't mean a thing to you, does it?' Nick asked harshly. 'You've put me through hell and laughed yourself sick at me. I couldn't bear what I thought you were. I despised myself for going crazy over a girl who went to bed at the drop of a hat.'

'I seem to remember you were more than ready to take whatever you thought you could get from me, for all your contempt,' Sara accused with a fierce anger.

His other hand came to grip her, the long fingers biting into her. 'You know why. Do you think I didn't hate myself? Do you think I didn't fight it? My God, the hours I've spent arguing with myself!'

'I can't recall seeing any signs of it,' Sara retorted, but the peculiar dancing elation which was coming into her was making her feel breathless. She looked at him secretly through her lashes. His face was pale, his eyes restless as he looked down at her.

'I told myself I'd stay away from you, but every time I saw you I lost control.' The hands on her arms slackened, the long fingers moved, stroked her gently. 'If I hadn't cared so much I could have gone to bed with you and forgotten it. I never cared before if there'd been others ahead of me. I can't remember it ever crossing my mind. I took what was offered and walked away without asking questions.'

'What a charming attitude!' Sara snapped then in trembling fury, lifting a flushed and angry face to him. How many others had there been for him? She spoke sharply, but her anger was not due to resentment of his double standards. She was jealous, stung. 'You had the right to play around as much as you liked, did you? And still cast it in my teeth because you thought I did the same? My God, that reveals the sort of mind you have!'

'Do you think I don't know that?'

'Hypocrite!' she spat bitterly.

His face whitened. 'Yes, I know.'

'I almost wish I'd been what you thought I was!'

'Don't,' he said with a hoarse gasp. 'Don't you know what you've done to me?'

The expression on his face frightened her sud-

denly. She moved as if to pull away and he caught
her back towards him, holding her rigidly again.

'I know you don't want to hear it. You've made
that plain. But I've got to tell you. Sara, for God's
sake, let me say it.'

She stood very still, head bent, and felt him staring down at her. 'I didn't think I'd ever see you
again,' he muttered suddenly. One of his hands
moved and removed the straw hat, dropped it to the
grass. Nick put a gentling hand to her hair, stroked
it. 'That night at the ballet you wouldn't even look
at me.' He put his head down abruptly, resting it on
her hair. 'It was making me ill to think of you with
other men. I couldn't live with the idea. I never
knew I had such a vivid imagination. Oh, God, my
imagination was working overtime!' She felt his
mouth move lightly against her forehead. 'It was the
most appalling relief when you came to the bank
and told me I'd been making myself ill over nothing.'

Sara forced herself to speak coolly. 'Well, I hope
it's taught you a lesson. Perhaps in future you won't
be so quick to jump to conclusions.'

He moved away, looking at her fiercely. 'You deliberately let me believe it right from the start.'

'I told you why.'

His eyes held hers. 'Yet whenever I touched you,
you responded,' he said huskily. 'Why?'

Her eyes fell, her flush deepening. She heard his
breathing quicken. 'Sara?' he asked shakily. He put
a hand under her chin, lifted her face, stared at her
searchingly.

She tried to avoid his stare, her green eyes mov-

ing away, and heard him give a sharp groan. Looking back, she saw his eyes half-closed, the blue gleam
of them flashing between his heavy lids, his skin taut
over his cheekbones. He looked dazed.

'Darling,' he said with his eyes fixed on her
mouth, then his face came down towards her. 'Oh,
God, let me kiss you.'

The sunlight was suddenly too bright. Her eyes
closed and she felt the heat of his mouth as it parted
hers, his arms clamping round her. Yielding, her
arms went round his neck, and felt him pull her
even closer, the hard insistent warmth of his body
pressing against her. His hands gripped her back,
caressed her possessively.

'I love you,' he whispered against her lips. 'My
darling, never turn away from me again—I couldn't
bear it. I don't know how I've managed to live
through the last year. You had me in such a state I
couldn't sleep, couldn't eat. I wanted you so much
I've been sick with it.'

Sara froze, pulling back, and he lifted his head,
his eyes flashing to her face.

'What is it? Sara . . .'

'I'm still not interested in an affair with you,' she
said with cold anger.

His smile was wry. 'I'm asking you to marry me,
don't you realise that?'

For a few seconds the happiness was like a golden
fountain, then her eyes went dead again. She shook
her head slowly.

'What do you mean, no?' Nick looked as though
she'd kicked him, his face taut.

'I can't.'

He bent towards her, speaking urgently. 'You don't care enough? I think you do, darling. You couldn't look at me like that if you weren't a little bit in love with me. Every time I kiss you, I get this tremendous response, don't you realise that?' His mouth had a shaking tenderness. 'You just don't know how you feel, Sara. Don't fight it. It means more than I can tell you.'

'All the same, it wouldn't work. We're hardly a computer match, are we? We come from very different worlds. We haven't anything going for us.'

He laughed huskily. 'Let me show you exactly what we have going for us,' he offered, his hands sliding down her spine.

'No, Nick,' she evaded, twisting away, but he pulled her back towards him remorselessly, bending his head. She put her hands on his chest to hold him away, struggling. Without using any extreme force Nick won the short struggle, bending her backwards slightly before his mouth came down on hers. He showed her at some length precisely what they had, and when at last she slackened the feverish grip of her arms around his neck, she was trembling and wildly flushed. He looked at her through sleepy, half-closed eyes, a passionate satisfaction in his face.

'My God, I've wanted to do that for a long time,' he groaned.

'I'd be mad to consider it!' Sara said with a smothered laugh.

His answering smile had rueful humour. 'That makes two of us. You're going to drive me out of my head, do you think I don't know that? You are the most maddening, infuriating hot-tempered little spitfire I've ever met. We're going to argue about every single, solitary thing under the sun, and I've no doubt I'm going to want to beat you more than once. But I just can't bear the thought of my life without you.'

'I don't see myself as a sedate banker's wife, ordering the fish and taking the dog for a walk,' Sara commented drily.

'Neither do I,' Nick agreed, his mouth twisting. He gave her a wicked little smile. 'But then my vision of our future is rather more hectic.'

She blushed and his blue eyes gleamed.

'Don't sidetrack,' she complained.

'I'm not. That's what matters, darling, can't you see?' His fingers found her neck, stroked it delicately, making shivers run down her spine. 'Marry me, Sara. If I just wanted to take you to bed, I wouldn't ask you, but it isn't just sex I want, it's you.' He looked at her with a passion that weakened her. 'All of you, even your stubborn, infuriating little mind. I want to live with you and that's something I've never wanted before. Seeing you here in the garden today, I knew life wasn't going to be worth living if I couldn't have you there whenever I looked up.'

He was saying what she secretly knew she felt herself. Nick was a part of her, woven indissolubly into her life, her heart. She needed him and she couldn't bear the thought of a future without him.

A new thought struck Sara. She groaned. 'If I married you, Tilly would insist on coming to live with us. I know it.'

Nick wore the complacency of one who knows

how much he's loved. 'Would you mind?'

'I know who'd be running the home,' Sara remarked drily.

'She's a darling, really,' Nick said. 'While you were painting Tilly would keep things ticking over for you.'

'You only look smug because you know she thinks the sun shines out of you.'

He didn't disagree, smiling. He was still holding her in his arms and the tension and urgency had drained out of him. The blue eyes were alight as they looked at her.

'Say it,' he suddenly muttered. 'You haven't said it yet. I told you, but you haven't told me.'

'What are you talking about?' she asked, genuinely bewildered.

The blue eyes glittered. 'You know what I want to hear you say.'

Her heart turned over. She closed her eyes and weakly laid her head on his shoulder, feeling the strength and hardness of the body under her cheek. 'I love you, Nick.'

He kissed her hair, trying to reach her face, but she burrowed it deeper into his body, and he laughed huskily.

'My darling, I don't believe it. Are you shy?'

'Regretful,' she groaned. 'It's insanity! We've nothing in common. We'll probably quarrel all day long.'

'At least I'll be able to get some sleep again,' Nick said, with apparent indifference to everything else.

'Listen,' said Sara, raising her head.

His mouth silenced whatever she had been about to say and her arms went round his neck to enclose him passionately.

Behind them the water rippled gently and the last of the sunshine turned the stream to liquid gold.

When they walked back to the house together Judith gave them a sly, wicked smile. Nick eyed her grimly.

'Ah, I want to have words with you, my dear sister.'

'I was just going to help Tilly with dinner,' Judith demurely evaded.

'Not so fast.' Nick caught her arm in an unbreakable grip. 'How did you know about Sara?'

Judith opened her eyes wide. 'Someone told me she was a very good landscape artist.'

Nick's lips compressed. 'What a liar you are, Judith. If I wasn't in an exceptionally good mood, I'd force it out of you like a cork out of a bottle. In future, keep your busy little nose out of my affairs.'

His sister looked at Sara, grinning. 'I seem to have done the trick, all the same.'

Nick looked down his nose, his face haughty. 'Spying, were you?'

'If you will behave in an abandoned fashion at the bottom of my garden, what else do you expect?' Judith asked sweetly.

Nick's arm went round Sara's waist, pulling her close to him. 'You can be the first to congratulate us, although you don't deserve it.'

Judith looked delighted, kissing them both. 'Thank the lord for that! I was afraid she'd turn you down and we'd have to put up with your nasty temper for life.'

'Very funny. I knew you'd be pleased,' Nick told her. 'David should beat you twice a day.'

'What a fantastic thought,' Judith returned shamelessly. 'Why not suggest it to him? David's never that inventive.'

Nick put his long hands over Sara's ears. 'You didn't hear that, my darling.'

Sara grinned at Judith. 'Of course not,' she responded demurely.

'Anyway,' Judith said with smug satisfaction, 'I think I deserve a vote of thanks, not censure. If I hadn't brought her here, you'd have gone around snarling and scowling for years without having the guts to do anything about it.'

Nick looked furious. Sara put a hand to his face, turning his head towards her.

'Go and help Tilly, Judith,' she murmured, looking into Nick's eyes. The door closed discreetly and Nick began to kiss her.

Dinner was a hilarious affair. Nick had opened a bottle of champagne, but by the time they had reached the second course it had all gone, so he opened another. Even Tilly had a smile which showed all her teeth in incredible detail. She looked smugly from Sara to Nick.

'Deciding how many children you'll have,' Judith whispered, careful to keep her tone too low for Tilly to catch.

Sara was too dazed with happiness and champagne to care. Every time her eyes met Nick's she felt her heart turn over with a wild flop like a fish in a basket, and Nick wasn't hiding how he felt. He kept looking at her, the blue eyes hungry, and Judith's elaborate plans for their wedding made him irritable.

'Do we need all that fuss?'

'Sara does,' Judith insisted. 'A girl only gets married once.' Her eyes teased Nick. 'Well, usually.'

'You were right first time,' he said with a bite, his eyes going again to Sara.

She yawned, suddenly heavy with sleep. Tilly eyed her. 'Bed for you,' she announced, and even Nick did not dare to argue.

Sara was barely aware of getting into bed. She fell asleep at once and slept deeply, her face flushed.

In the morning she woke to find three small dark heads ranged along the end of her bed, their chins resting on the wooden rail.

'Hallo, you monsters,' she greeted them, yawning.

'It's raining,' they told her. 'We can't go out in the garden. There's sausages for breakfast if you get down before Uncle Nick eats them all.'

'Well, clear off and let me dress,' she invited.

When she came down she found Nick at the breakfast table with a newspaper in his hands and the remains of a hearty breakfast before him. He looked round, his face lighting up, and she bent with her hand on his shoulder to kiss him.

Tilly popped her head round the door and Sara straightened. 'Good morning, Tilly.'

'There's one sausage left. What those boys didn't get, he did.'

'Pig,' Sara informed Nick. 'I'll have toast, Tilly.'

'I'll make it now,' said Tilly. 'Sure you won't have an egg?'

'No, thank you. Just toast.'

Tilly vanished and Nick pulled Sara back down to him, his hands on her slim waist.

'You taste of marmalade,' she told him. 'I hope you won't always taste of it, because I'm not addicted to the stuff.'

'I love you,' he told her in reply. 'I've been waiting for you to come down because I had an awful feeling I'd dreamt it all.'

She laughed. 'No, it wasn't a dream, or if it was, I dreamt it too.'

'When will you marry me?'

'When Judith has decided on a date,' Sara teased.

'Seriously,' Nick said.

'We'll discuss it when Greg gets back to London.'

His face changed. 'I wish you weren't so hung-up on Halliday,' he muttered. 'I accept you aren't in love with him, but you and he are too damned close.'

'Greg lives and breathes for Lucy, I promise you. He worries about me because he brought me up and I worry about him because there was never anybody else in my life. When he marries Lucy she can worry about him.'

'So long as you don't,' said Nick, not hiding the jealousy in his dark face. His eyes lingered on her possessively and Sara gave him a contented smile, happy to have him look at her like that. However insane it was to marry him, she knew she had no

real choice. Her choice had been made long ago on
the evening they met, although at that time she had
been thinking of nothing but Greg, barely aware of
Nick at the time.

Oddly, it seemed Nick was thinking of that evening, too, his face hardening.

'You remember the night we met? That was
when I started thinking you loved Halliday. I saw
the way you couldn't keep your eyes off him and
even then I was jealous. I wanted to stop you looking at him. I wanted to make you look at me. I didn't
know what was happening to me, but I was determined to make you see me.'

'Poor Greg, he was so unhappy that night.' She
looked at Nick soberly. 'You've got to like him,
Nick. I couldn't bear it if there was trouble between
you two. You both mean so much to me.'

Nick's frown came and went. 'I'll try not to hate
his guts,' he said wryly.

'You wouldn't be jealous if he really was my
brother,' she pointed out.

He grimaced. 'No? I'm not so sure. I never remember being jealous in my life before, but since
I met you I've been forced to recognise my own
capacity for it. I think I'd be jealous of anyone you
looked at.' He laughed, his mouth harsh. 'Even Forcell. I've given him hell for weeks, poor fellow. He
looks bewildered whenever he sees me.'

'Oh, poor Jeremy,' Sara said, laughing.

'Poor Jeremy hell!' Nick at once looked furious.
'When he kissed you yesterday I nearly threw him
bodily into the stream.'

She laughed. 'You're surprisingly violent for a banker, Nick.'

'Then we're more evenly matched than you think,' Nick said forcibly. 'Because you aren't exactly a model of sweet temper yourself. I'm not blind to your faults.'

She looked at him teasingly. 'What faults? I'm perfect.'

His eyes glimmered. 'Oh? Now I'd have said you were an atrocious flirt, for a start.'

'Me?' She opened her green eyes wide.

'Yes, you, my butter-wouldn't-melt-in-the-mouth darling. I've watched you flirt too many times to be convinced you're not. You have a way of looking at men which sends their temperatures up.'

Her face sobered. Was he returning to his original ideas about her? He caught her eyes and smiled at her wryly.

'No, I'm not harking back. I believe you've never gone further than flirting, but don't expect me to like watching you smile like that at other men. I know precisely what that smile of yours can do, remember.'

'If you've finished cataloguing my faults, I might begin on yours,' she said sweetly, smiling at him in exactly the fashion he had just complained about, and Nick's hand shot over the table to grab hers. He lifted it to his mouth and bent his head, his lips hungrily pressing the pink palm.

She drew a shaky breath at the passion in his face and he looked at her, his face urgent.

'Marry me soon,' he muttered.

The door opened with ostentatious slowness and Judith came in, coughing a loud stage cough. Nick released Sara's hand and leaned back, giving his sister an ironic, deriding smile.

'Very funny, but we were doing nothing we shouldn't.'

'I should hope not, over sausages and toast,' Judith returned, unabashed. She dropped a kiss on his hair, came round to kiss Sara's cheek. 'Tilly did mutter something about passion at breakfast time being disgusting, though.'

Nick slid Sara a grin. 'Oh, that wasn't me,' he said mockingly. 'Tilly saw Sara kiss me when she came down, that's all.'

Judith gave him a beatific smile. 'You'll be needing Tilly when you're married, won't you? Sara won't want to give up her work to keep house.'

Nick eyed her grimly. 'Don't think I can't read your mind like a particularly revolting book. I'm well aware what was behind your sudden devotion to my happiness. You got Sara down here in the hope of getting me married off and Tilly out of your hair.'

Judith's eyes were wide and innocent. 'What are you talking about? Can't I get my garden painted without vile accusations being bandied about?'

'How did you find out about Sara?' he demanded.

'You must have been a tracker dog in some previous existence,' his sister complained.

'How, Judith?'

She looked at him drily. 'You were rather obvious

that day at the Zoo. I saw you looking at her and I put two and two together.'

He flushed. 'That still doesn't explain how you found her.'

Sara bit into her toast, watching Judith over it. Judith looked at Nick with sweet transparency and lied without flinching. 'I saw a picture of her in a newspaper.'

'Oh,' said Nick, accepting it. He looked at Judith menacingly. 'Well, in future, mind your own business.'

She gave him a cheerful grin. 'I'm sorry if I made a mistake in getting her down here. I thought you'd be delighted to see her.'

Nick's flush deepened. 'Who the hell invented families?' he demanded of the ceiling.

'I had the impression you were all set to add another family to the world,' Judith observed, lips twitching. 'In fact, I thought you couldn't wait to do so.'

Nick lowered his gaze. 'Haven't you got anything else to do? Why don't you go and fuss over one of your loathsome offspring?'

'Charming,' said Judith, looking from him to Sara. 'When Sara has finished her breakfast, why don't you take her for a drive? Then maybe I can have my own home back.'

Nick looked at Sara restlessly. 'Coming, darling?'

She finished her toast and drank the last of her coffee. 'Coming,' she said, getting up.

Tilly stopped them in the hall, her limp exaggerated. 'Andrew's put his Batcar down the waste disposal and it's making noises like a concrete mixer.'

'Tell Judith,' said Nick with satisfaction. 'I'm taking Sara for a drive. This house is worse than Piccadilly Circus!'

As they drove away Sara was laughing and Nick glanced down at her, his black brows lifted. 'What's funny now?'

'Life,' Sara said vaguely. 'I had such a different picture of you, Nick. Your penthouse, the bank, the lovely ladies you squire around ... that was what I knew of you until Judith brought me down here, but you're very different here. I never thought I'd see you being chivvied around the way Tilly does.'

'We're all of us contradictory,' Nick shrugged.

Sara sighed. 'But I barely know you, do you realise that? Oh, Nick, are we quite mad to think of getting married knowing so little about each other?'

'We know enough. I think I knew that first night at the party. I hadn't recognised the way I felt, but I'd been watching you for some time, before I managed to wangle an introduction, and I couldn't stop looking at you.' He glanced sideways, smiling, his eyes wandering from her bright head to her small, vivacious face. 'You're like sunshine. You sparkle. And when you smile I get a strange feeling inside me as though I'd just drunk champagne. What drove me mad was the thought that you'd smiled at other men like that.'

'I can't say I enjoy the fact that you've known

other women,' Sara admitted, her face wry as she let
her secret jealousy show.

His eyes widened and a smile came into them.
'Ah,' he said softly, watching her.

She lifted her chin aggressively. 'What does "Ah"
mean?'

'I wondered if it bothered you,' he admitted.

'What do you think?'

He took her hand, lifted it to his lips and kissed
it. 'There'll never be anyone else. There hasn't been
for a long time, not since I recognised the way I felt.
It took me a while to face it, but by the night you
came to my flat I knew for certain. I almost went
crazy when you walked out on me that night. If I'd
seen Halliday after that I really think I might have
killed him.'

She regarded him oddly. 'Believing that I was living with Greg I'm surprised you still wanted me.'

His mouth tautened. 'You're surprised? I was dis-
gusted with myself. I tried never to see you. I really
fought it. But when I saw you at Annabel's party,
it started up again. I didn't give a damn that night
how many others there were. Once I had you alone
I knew I'd take anything you let me take.'

Her face wry, she shook her head at him. 'How
unprincipled!'

'Weak,' he supplemented. 'You had me on my
knees.' His eyes held hers as he slowed and pulled
into a leaf-shaded layby. He turned, his arm along
the seat, smiling. 'And you knew it, didn't you?'

The green eyes danced. She put a lazy finger on

his cheek, smiling. 'I knew you fancied me. That was obvious.'

His smile vanished. 'Yes,' he said in a low voice. 'After you came to the bank I realised just what I'd done. If I hadn't made such a heavy pass at you in the beginning, you wouldn't have let me go on thinking you were Halliday's mistress, would you? I dug my own grave. My God, I hated knowing that!' A hard red lay along his cheekbones, the blue eyes were self-condemning. 'When you wouldn't see me, speak to me, I only had myself to blame. I deserved these last weeks, darling, but I went through hell.'

She could see that. The shadow of that pain lay in his eyes now. He had lost weight, his face more forceful and fleshless than ever. Sara touched his cheek again, looking into his eyes.

'Did we stop to have another post-mortem?'

Nick's face lightened, his smile flashing out. 'You know why we stopped,' he said, pulling her over into his arms. 'Come here, you thorn in my flesh.' His hands framed her laughing face. 'I promised myself a long time ago that one day I'd kiss the smile right off your face. You've laughed at me once too often.'

His mouth closed over hers possessively and Sara stopped smiling, but inside her the laughter spread out like oxygen through her blood, dancing and exulting, until with a sudden clamour passion cut off everything but a blind response which had her trembling in Nick's arms under the shadowy trees.

The Mills & Boon Rose is the Rose of Romance

Every month there are ten new titles to choose from — ten new stories about people falling in love, people you want to read about, people in exciting, far away places. Choose Mills & Boon. It's your way of relaxing.

January's titles are:

BED OF GRASS by *Janet Dailey*
Judd Prescott had been the reason for Valerie leaving home. Now she was back, but Judd still didn't know what that reason had been ...

WINTER WEDDING by *Betty Neels*
Professor Renier Jurres-Romeijn regarded Emily as a 'prim miss'. So it wasn't surprising that he so obviously preferred her lively sister Louise.

DANGEROUS DECEPTION by *Lilian Peake*
Anona Willis was engaged to the forceful Shane Brodie — but he had admitted that he had no staying power where women were concerned ...

FEVER by *Charlotte Lamb*
The attraction between Sara Nichols and Nick Rawdon was immediate — but somehow Sara could never clear up the misunderstanding about her stepbrother Greg.

SWEET HARVEST by *Kerry Allyne*
Any thought of a reconciliation between herself and her husband soon vanished when Alix realised that Kirby had chosen her successor ...

STAY THROUGH THE NIGHT by *Flora Kidd*
Virtually kidnapped aboard Burt Sharaton's yacht, Charlotte was told that if she didn't co-operate with him, he would ruin her father ...

HELL OR HIGH WATER by *Anne Mather*
Jarret Manning was attractive, successful, experienced — and Helen Chase felt mingled antagonism and fear every time she met this disturbing man.

CANDLE IN THE WIND by *Sally Wentworth*
Shipwrecked, her memory lost, Sam had to believe her companion Mike Scott when he told her she was his wife ...

WHITE FIRE by *Jan MacLean*
Rana had fallen wildly in love with Heath Markland, to the fury of her domineering mother. But perhaps she knew something about Heath that Rana didn't ...

A STREAK OF GOLD by *Daphne Clair*
Eight years ago, Ric Burnett had cruelly told Glenna to get out of his life — but now they had met again ...

If you have difficulty in obtaining any of these books from your local paperback retailer, write to:

Mills and Boon Reader Service
P.O. Box No 236, Thornton Road, Croydon, Surrey CR9 3RU

The Mills & Boon Rose is the Rose of Romance

Look for the Rose of Romance this Christmas

Four titles by favourite authors in a specially-produced gift pack.

THAT BOSTON MAN *by Janet Dailey*

MY SISTER'S KEEPER *by Rachel Lindsay*

ENEMY FROM THE PAST *by Lilian Peake*

DARK DOMINION *by Charlotte Lamb*

UNITED KINGDOM £2.20 net
REP. OF IRELAND £2.40

First time in paperback.
Still available from your local paperback retailer.

190